THE LOCKER NEXT 2 MINE

A full-length dramedy by
Jonathan Dorf

For Matt,
All best wishes!
Jonathan Df

www.youthplays.com
info@youthplays.com
424-703-5315

CAST OF CHARACTERS

TV REPORTER, Cyndi Jackson, an adult, could also be male.

BRADY, former high school TV news reporter and a junior. We meet him as the Teen Reporter in the opening scene.

ALISA, female, same age, new student.

HEADLINE, a sophomore boy who speaks in news headlines.

BUY BOY (aka Tanner), male, the school's resident wheeler-dealer.

LUNA, female, not a real-time character and revealed in the end to be Beth.

MARNE, female, high school senior and leader of the M squad.

MIRANDA, female, and perhaps the most cutthroat member of the M squad.

MELISSA, female, third member of the M squad.

DALTON, male, varsity lacrosse player.

CHUCK, male, barely a JV lacrosse player.

QE, female, Beth's younger sister.

SABRINA, female, friend of Jeremy.

HABIT, female, friend of Jeremy.

LEGOLAS, male whose real name is Aloysius, friend of Jeremy.

SUBSTITUTE TEACHER, either gender.

MARIO, male.

WENDY, aspiring actress.

PAM, female.

GIGGLING GIRL

ROXANNA, female, student council president.

FIRST NEEDY STUDENT, either gender.

SECOND NEEDY STUDENT, either gender.

THIRD NEEDY STUDENT, either gender.

FOURTH NEEDY STUDENT, either gender.

MRS. LOIS (or LOUIS) IGNORA, secretary.

DR. COPPERFIELD, male but could be female.

HYACINTH KROY, female, student TV reporter.

CAR KID, male but could be female.

VANESSA, female, Beth's best friend and a lacrosse player.

CHORUS OF STUDENTS, could be a separate group of students or double cast with students in featured roles.

CHORUS OF MASKED TEACHERS, can be played by students.

LOU, female, a shortened version of Louise.

DANIELLE, producer for the student TV station (this character could also be Daniel, male).

To keep cast size down, many roles may be doubled. While Miranda's last name is mentioned as Conway, it could be updated to reflect the actress' ethnicity (Martinez, Chang, etc.). Ditto the last names of Marne and Melissa. All adult characters are masked, to further isolate the play's teens.

ACKNOWLEDGEMENTS

The Locker Next 2 Mine was commissioned by Wantagh High School Theatre Department (Wantagh, NY) "in the sincere hope that no school will ever again have a Pluto problem." First produced by The Randolph School (Huntsville, AL).

SCENE 1

(A dark stage. Out of the darkness comes a CHORUS OF STUDENTS, with no one voice speaking two lines in a row. At some point the lights could come up to reveal the performers, or the entire scene could play in darkness.)

CHORUS OF STUDENTS: We miss you, Elizabeth.
We'll never forget you.

TV REPORTER: *(Wearing a mask:)* The scene is grim here on this poorly lit back road—

CHORUS OF STUDENTS: We love you, Beth.

TEEN REPORTER: Beth Turner, lacrosse co-captain—

CHORUS OF STUDENTS: First in our hearts.

TV REPORTER: Police tape and flowers and teddy bears mark the spot—

CHORUS OF STUDENTS: We dedicate this season—
This year—
This forever...

TV REPORTER: The irony of a lacrosse star—

TEEN REPORTER: I don't think I can do this.

CHORUS OF STUDENTS: You'll always be—
Always—
First in our hearts-

TEEN REPORTER: I report on dances and mystery meat—

TV REPORTER: The car coming to a stop a mere 1000 feet from a field—

TEEN REPORTER: This is too real.

CHORUS OF STUDENTS: Always—
First—

Always be with us.

TEEN REPORTER: I'm sorry.

TV REPORTER: Just like the one that was home to some of her greatest triumphs.

TEEN REPORTER: *(Exiting:)* Somebody else has to do this.

CHORUS OF STUDENTS: Now —
Always —
Forever —

(Becoming softer:)

Always...
Always...
Always...

(The lights slowly come up on a school hallway. ALISA, high school junior, tries to open a locker. It's not easy, because she is squeezed on one side by a sprawling shrine of teddy bears, flowers, sports trophies, handwritten notes and cards, including a prominent written pronouncement that "We Love Beth." It's all centered in front of the locker directly next to hers. Beat. HEADLINE, male and a year younger, observes her struggles, gradually moving closer.)

HEADLINE: New Student Arrives at Washington High School. *(Beat.)* New Student Battles the Shrine.

ALISA: *(Losing hold of her books:)* What?

HEADLINE: Shrine Wins! Shrine Wins!

ALISA: Who are you?

(Enter BUY BOY, Alisa's age, and the guy you go to when you need to buy or sell pretty much anything.)

BUY BOY: That's how he talks.

HEADLINE: *(Helping pick up Alisa's books:)* Knight in Shining Armor Saves the Day!

BUY BOY: I got it.

(Buy Boy competes with Headline for Alisa's books.)

HEADLINE: Superhero Rescues Fair Maiden in School Hallway!

BUY BOY: I said I got it.

ALISA: *(Pulling the books away from them:)* I've got them.

BUY BOY: Just trying to help.

ALISA: Thanks. I'm OK. It's just this...

(She gestures toward the shrine.)

HEADLINE: Shrine Claims Next Victim.

ALISA: *(To Headline:)* Can you stop that?

BUY BOY: *(Making a move toward Headline:)* Headline, stop being a freak.

(Headline retreats.)

HEADLINE: Hero Vows to Return!

(Headline exits.)

BUY BOY: Sorry 'bout that.

ALISA: What's wrong with him?

BUY BOY: Last year, there was this...thing, and he just started talking like that.

ALISA: *(Indicates the shrine:)* This, uh...thing?

BUY BOY: No. *(Holds out his hand:)* Tanner. But you can call me Buy Boy.

ALISA: Why?

BUY BOY: You want to buy, I'm sellin'.

ALISA: Buy what?

BUY BOY: Anything.

ALISA: Are you a narc?

BUY BOY: I'm not a dealer. Not that kind.

ALISA: Good to know.

BUY BOY: You need anything, I take cash or credit. Gimme your name and I'll even give you the friends and family discount.

ALISA: That's OK.

BUY BOY: Negotiation—I like it. *(Beat.)* How about I give you the friends and family discount, and you think about giving me your name?

ALISA: *(Beat.)* Alisa.

　　(A BELL RINGS.)

BUY BOY: I'll see you later, Alisa.

　　(The hallway floods with STUDENTS.)

ALISA: *(Gesturing toward the shrine:)* What about this...?

　　(But he's gone. Lights dim on the pack of students in the hallway, and up on LUNA. She is alone and in her own light, but she should be lit in such a way that her face is somewhat hidden. It's an out of time moment.)

LUNA: Pluto was officially discovered in 1930. It became the ninth planet, and the farthest from the sun. What a lot of people don't know—no, what pretty much everybody doesn't know, is that its orbit crosses Neptune's, the eighth planet, but the two planets don't ever come close to each other. *(Beat.)* So Pluto's always been this lonely little planet, and it's cold. Really, really cold. Like negative 230 degrees Celsius cold. People couldn't live there. *(Beat.)* I'm pretty sure most people don't spend a lot of time thinking about Pluto. Why would you? Pluto doesn't get you an A in English or pay your car insurance or keep your mom from aiming a half full coffee mug at your dad's head on the last night you pretended you had a functional family. *(Beat.)* But then it happened. In 2006, Pluto got demoted. One day it's a planet, and the next day it's not. They come up with this new category: a dwarf planet. Sure, Pluto, you're separate but equal. Right. And finally people take notice. Harvard students stage a sit-in at University Hall, in Berkeley they burn a revised map of the solar system and protestors take to the streets of Manhattan to stand up for Pluto. *(Beat.)* I made that last part up. Outside of a few astronomers, nobody really cared, and after a few weeks, people stopped talking about it. Nobody ever stands up for the Plutos of the universe. At least not in my universe. *(Beat.)* Our school has a Pluto problem.

> *(Luna disappears back into the crowd of passing students as the stage begins to transition into the cafeteria. WENDY, the class drama geek in a non-geeky way, slips in just ahead of MARNE [pronounced Mar-nee], MELISSA and MIRANDA, a trio of popular girls nicknamed "The M Squad," who know just how popular they are. They wear black T-shirts emblazoned with "Elizabeth Turner – Always in Our Hearts." They have Beth's picture on the front. Marne carries a bag of T-shirts. They accost students heading into the cafeteria, passing out flyers.)*

WENDY: Get your Shake on this Saturday and Sunday! That's right—fall hard for the Bard as girls play boys and boys play girls in our revolutionary new version of Richard II.

MARNE: Friday night vigil. *(Shoving a flyer into a student's* *hand:)* Be there. There's gonna be food trucks.

MELISSA: One-year anniversary. Better be there.

(Miranda shoves a flyer into the hands of DALTON, wearing a lacrosse jersey over his otherwise preppy attire. CHUCK, not nearly cool enough to be Dalton's friend and going through an array of protein shakes and bars in a vain attempt to keep up, looks like he wants to worship the ground Marne walks on.)

MIRANDA: You *will* be there.

CHUCK: Hey, Marne.

(Marne doesn't appear to be aware of his existence.)

DALTON: You know I never miss.

MELISSA: Except for last month.

MIRANDA: Show love, Dalton.

DALTON: Can I show *you* love?

MIRANDA: *(Nuzzling up to him to tease:)* I would love you more stylin' the new all-black.

CHUCK: All-black would mean black letters too.

MIRANDA: Chuck!

MELISSA: Don't be stupid.

MIRANDA: Don't be an ass.

MELISSA: Stupid ass.

CHUCK: Uh...it was a joke. Marne, you know it was a joke, right?

MARNE: How many T-shirts you own, Chuck?

CHUCK: I've got one.

MARNE: Never seen it. *(To Miranda:)* You seen it?

MELISSA: *(Jumping in:)* Nopesters.

MIRANDA: Never seen it.

CHUCK: I think I got it in like September. Or October.

MIRANDA: You think?

MELISSA: Better be sure.

MARNE: When I *think* about it, don't remember seeing you at a vigil.

CHUCK: I've been. *(Pause.)* Dalton, tell 'em I've been.

DALTON: How much for the all-black?

MARNE: Fifteen.

> *(Dalton forks over the cash. They hand him a T-shirt. As they do, lights up on QE [pronounced Q.E.], Beth's younger sister, standing across the cafeteria. To Chuck:)*

Go tell QE you don't want to buy a shirt.

CHUCK: No, it's not that —

MIRANDA: What is it?

MARNE: Dalton, put that shirt on.

CHUCK: Things are just a little tight right now.

MARNE: Beth is dead.

CHUCK: I know.

> *(Dalton takes his jersey off and puts the shirt on.)*

MARNE: And if you cared about her —

MELISSA: Like Dalton.

MIRANDA: You'd be puttin' on that all-black.

CHUCK: I care. I'm just tapped.

MARNE: Sacrifice a freakin' protein shake.

MELISSA: Not like it's helping.

CHUCK: What about those buttons?   I have enough for a button.

MARNE: Sold out months ago.

MIRANDA: You look hot, Dalton.

MELISSA: Red hot.

MARNE: *(To Chuck:)* Go tell QE you hate her sister.

CHUCK: But I don't—

MELISSA: Or we will.

CHUCK: I get paid next Friday.

MIRANDA: Next Friday's really far from this Friday.

MELISSA: Like another country.

MARNE: And the vigil's *this* Friday.

MIRANDA: Everyone, can I have your attention?

MELISSA: Listen up, people: Chuckie's got something to say.

(The cafeteria starts to go quiet.)

CHUCK: Why are you doing this?

MARNE: Because we can.

MELISSA: QE, you'll want to hear this.

CHUCK: OK!

QE: *(From across the cafeteria:)* Hear what?

MIRANDA: Nah—it's all good, QE. We love you, girl.

(Marne gestures for people to go back to what they were doing. The noise level returns.)

MARNE: *(To Chuck:)* Let me see that 20.

CHUCK: It's 15, right?

MARNE: Twenty.

CHUCK: But—

MELISSA: Did she stutter?

CHUCK: *(Beat — indicating the cafeteria:)* That's all I got for the week.

MIRANDA: Tell that to QE.

(Chuck digs for money and pays off Marne. Beat.)

CHUCK: Hope you're happy.

MARNE: It's not about me.

(Miranda or Melissa gives Chuck a T-shirt, or rather tosses it at him. The lights shift to focus on QE:)

QE: I'm used to being on the other end of those looks. Those poor QE looks. Those "insert name here" Beth's sister looks. I run from memorial to vigil to dedication to fundraiser. It's like all Beth, all the time. Nobody even knows me. Well, everybody knows me. I'm Beth's sister. *(Beat.)* After they had Beth—Elizabeth—they had *Queen* Elizabeth. Seriously? It's what you name your toy poodle. But nobody says a thing anymore. It took my sister dying to make my lifetime humiliation of a name cool. And how am I supposed to change it now? How am I supposed to change any of this?

(QE melts into the crowds of the cafeteria. Alisa looks for a table. Headline comes up to her.)

HEADLINE: Beautiful Princess Sits with Charming, Handsome Prince.

(He pulls out a chair for her, offering the seat, brushing off the

table at the last minute when he realizes it's dirty. Buy Boy intercepts Alisa.)

BUY BOY: You don't want to sit there.

ALISA: And you know this because...?

(Alisa turns away from both of them. Lights up on the outcast table, populated by SABRINA, perhaps a goth; LEGOLAS, whose real name is Aloysius, and HABIT, short for nothing and often quiet. In between them sits a burger with ketchup and relish, alone on a plate. They each raise a glass:)

SABRINA: To Jeremy.

(Sabrina's words arrest Headline's attention. He looks like he wants to come over, but lingers where he is, watching their exchange from a distance. Habit tips her glass in the direction of the burger.)

LEGOLAS: To J-Bird.

SABRINA: He hated that name

LEGOLAS: No he didn't.

SABRINA: Yes he did.

LEGOLAS: *(To Habit:)* Tiebreaker?

(Habit nods and gestures to Sabrina, tipping the vote to her. Beat.)

He never said anything.

SABRINA: Kinda had other stuff.

LEGOLAS: *(Quietly:)* Yeah. *(Beat – to the burger:)* Sorry, Jeremy.

SABRINA: Not like he spent days on end saying, "Oh my God, will Legolas stop calling me J-Bird?"

LEGOLAS: *(Beat.)* He didn't say that, did he?

SABRINA: I just said, "It's not like he did."

LEGOLAS: So that's a no?

SABRINA: Doesn't matter now.

LEGOLAS: Can't you just give me one straight answer?!

SABRINA: No! He said it once and that was it.

LEGOLAS: What did he say?

SABRINA: I didn't write it down.

LEGOLAS: Was he like really angry?

SABRINA: He said, "I'm only killing myself because I can't kill Legolas."

LEGOLAS: That's not funny.

SABRINA: Sorry. Just tryin to be a mood lifter. Memorial Cheeseburger Wednesday.

LEGOLAS: Yeah, they do get kind of downer.

SABRINA: *(Beat.)* You get your paper done?

LEGOLAS: Almost. Worked on it all last night.

SABRINA: Isn't it due tomorrow?

LEGOLAS: One more all-nighter should do it. *(Beat.)* So what did he say?

SABRINA: You're still on that?

LEGOLAS: I just need to know.

SABRINA: *(Beat.)* I don't know. It was something like, "Why does Legolas call me that stupid nickname?"

LEGOLAS: He said it was stupid? *(Beat.)* I would have

stopped. I would have stopped in a second.

SABRINA: I know.

LEGOLAS: Why didn't you say something?

SABRINA: *(Mostly to herself:)* Why didn't I say something about a lot of things?

(Habit steps out of real time.)

HABIT: Dalton beats the crap out of his liver every Friday and Saturday night. I know this. The M Squad likes shopping, gossip and guys in that order. Every study hall, perfect little Marne's got one tab open to some fashion page and the other to DidYouHearAboutHim.com. Tanner, Buy Boy, whatever his name is—he's always makin' a deal and scratchin' out an extra buck, and his mom and dad have his and hers Porsches. He just can't help it. It's a habit. *(Beat.)* You notice habits are mostly bad? Like silence. That's mine. And it's mostly bad.

(Habit steps back into the scene just as Marne's posse arrives at her table, but for once, Marne doesn't seem to be steering them there.)

MIRANDA: Listen up, freakazoids.

MARNE: Leave it.

MELISSA: Why?

MARNE: You know why.

MIRANDA: Not really.

MELISSA: The three little freaklets ought to get with the program.

MARNE: They will.

MIRANDA: When?

MELISSA: *(Beat.)* She wears all black anyway.

MARNE: Let's just go. I want a latte.

MIRANDA: You hate lattes.

MARNE: Whatever. A cappuccino.

(Beat. Melissa and Miranda exchange a look between them, while Marne has just a moment of connection with Habit, Legolas and Sabrina. The M Squad moves on.)

LEGOLAS: You ever wonder about the cheeseburger?

SABRINA: I wonder if it's dog.

LEGOLAS: Aside from that.

SABRINA: What am I supposed to wonder about? You shouldn't think about things too much.

LEGOLAS: Well, like we never eat it.

HABIT: I'm a vegetarian.

LEGOLAS: Yeah, but if you weren't.

HABIT: But I am.

SABRINA: What are you wondering about?

LEGOLAS: If we eat the cheeseburger, is that like at communion when they eat the body of Christ?

SABRINA: You mean like Jeremy is the cheeseburger and if we eat it, we're eating his body?

LEGOLAS: Symbolically.

HABIT: I'm only eating him if he's tofu. *(Beat.)* I shouldn't speak.

SABRINA: This conversation is so messed up.

HABIT: Dumb things come out when I speak.

SABRINA: No — this is *all* so messed up.

LEGOLAS: Just like every single day.

(They do not eat the burger. Headline looks like every ounce of his being wants to go over to them, but instead he exits as the lights dim on them and come up on Alisa, trying to find a seat at last. She finds an open seat by Brady, the Teen Reporter from the first scene.)

ALISA: Is anyone sitting here?

(He shakes his head. She sits.)

Hi. I'm Alisa.

BRADY: Brady.

ALISA: Nice to meet you.

BRADY: You too.

ALISA: I brought my lunch. Didn't know if the food was good or *(Beat.)* Seems like everybody at this school...either you can't shut them up or they hardly talk at all.

BRADY: Sorry. *(Looking up from his lunch:)* How are you? How's that?

ALISA: Good.

BRADY: You're good, or I'm doing good? *(Corrects himself:)* Well.

ALISA: Don't worry about it.

BRADY: What am I not worrying about? *(Beat.)* Too much now?

ALISA: You're doing fine. Mid-year transfers suck, but other than this crazy shrine next to my locker that I'm going to trip over really, really soon and the two guys hitting on me in front of it, in the caff and everywhere else they see me, I'm great.

BRADY: Don't worry. I won't hit on you.

ALISA: Gay, or just not your type?

BRADY: No confidence.

ALISA: Oh. *(Beat.)* Well, maybe you could borrow some from one of them. They have way too much. *(Beat.)* Not that I'm telling you to hit on me. That came out wrong.

BRADY: It's cool. I think I know what you meant. *(Beat.)* I used to have it.

ALISA: What happened?

BRADY: Bell's about to ring. Better beat the herd.

> *(He gets up abruptly and exits as the BELL RINGS. Alisa finds herself thrown into a three-ring circus. Each of these lines should be delivered by a different speaker, so that no one delivers two lines in a row.)*

CHORUS OF STUDENTS: Welcome to Washington High School, where we offer a wide variety of sports and clubs.
Activities.
There's marching band, newspaper, animals rights and recycling, P.E. leadership, Varsity Key Club—
Of course, if you arrive in the middle of the year, your options are limited.
You've missed fall sports.
Winters's going, going gone.
You'll probably be such a mess academically that you won't have time to participate.
Or have a social life.
But if you do, things are kinda set already.
Debate partners are picked.
The fall play is over.
The spring play is practically cast.

(A student posts a cast list.)

Model UN, done.
Math club, done.
Science Olympiad, check;
Geekdom organizes way early.
Technically, those are nerds.
And if you find a club that you can get into, everybody's known each other for a thousand years.
You're on the outside looking in.
You wish you were that close.
Let's face it — your life is a total cluster —
Beep!

(The throng of students disperses, and we're left with Alisa trying to get at her locker. She measures her path, but doesn't quite have the coordination for success. Beat. She gives the closest parts of the shrine a nudge, trying to buy herself some breathing room. Enter Marne, Miranda and Melissa. Alisa stops her efforts, but too late.)

MARNE: What's up?

ALISA: Not much.

MELISSA: Pretty amazing, isn't it.

ALISA: What?

MIRANDA: *(Indicates the shrine:)* This.

ALISA: Yeah.

MARNE: So what are you doing?

ALISA: What do you mean?

MELISSA: We're not blind.

ALISA: I almost fell.

MIRANDA: Do you know what this is?

ALISA: I barely touched it.

MIRANDA: I said do you know what this is.

ALISA: I can't get to my locker. What am I supposed to do?

MARNE: You're new here, right?

ALISA: Yeah. I'm A—

MARNE: You should figure out what's what before you start messing with things.

ALISA: I'm not trying to mess with things. I'm just trying to get to my locker.

MELISSA: Who gave you the right to touch things?

ALISA: If they moved it six inches... *(Trying to lighten the mood:)* I'm just not that coordinated.

MARNE: Maybe it's you that needs to move.

MIRANDA: Hate to see something bad happen...

ALISA: What?

MELISSA: Did she stutter?

ALISA: Are you threa—

MARNE: *(As they sweep off:)* Leaving.

   (They exit, leaving Alisa shaken.)

SCENE 2

(A classroom. A SUBSTITUTE TEACHER passes back aptitude tests. Half of them are already in students' hands. Dalton leans over to Chuck.)

DALTON: Sub. We should blow this off.

CHUCK: Thanks for screwing me.

DALTON: Come on. It's a sub.

SUBSTITUTE TEACHER: Aloysius—

LEGOLAS: *(Cutting her off, but not before a snicker or two escapes from the peanut gallery:)* Legolas.

(He goes and gets his results. As the scene continues, the Substitute Teacher passes out the rest of the tests, her lips moving as if she's calling out names.)

DALTON: *(Beat.)* You're not seriously still mad about the shirt.

(Chuck holds up his hand, as in "talk to the hand," and ignores him. Across the room, MARIO holds up his results in disbelief.)

MARIO: I'm going to be a non-union plumber.

WENDY: You're what?

(Wendy grabs them out of his hand.)

MARIO: It says I'm best suited to be a non-union plumber.

WENDY: An aptitude test can tell you that?

MARIO: Why am I not good enough to be in the union?

WENDY: Maybe you're not a joiner.

MARIO: But non-union plumbers don't make near as much money.

(PAM chimes in.)

PAM: It says I should be a veterinarian.

WENDY: You're gonna make a lot more money than Mario.

MARIO: Shut up.

PAM: But I'm allergic to cats. And dogs.

MARIO: *(To Wendy:)* What'd yours say?

WENDY: Actress.

MARIO: No way.

WENDY: Well, basically.

PAM: What'd it say?

WENDY: Waitress. But that's such an obvious stepping stone to actress...I'm thinking of inviting the entire test advisory board to see me play Henry this weekend—

ALISA: *(To Brady:)* Should I ask—

BRADY: Don't.

WENDY: —just so they can see it for themselves—

ALISA: *(Beat.)* These things mean nothing.

BRADY: Tell that to my parents.

WENDY: —and recalibrate those tests.

BRADY: You're lucky you don't have one.

ALISA: So far, the only good thing about being new.

BRADY: Hey!

ALISA: Almost only thing.

SUBSTITUTE TEACHER: *(Pronounced rhine-er:)* Jeremy Reiner.

(The class goes silent.)

MARIO: *(Uncomfortably:)* Oh man...

CHUCK: How's he still on the roster?

DALTON: You talking to me now?

SUBSTITUTE TEACHER: Is Jeremy absent?

BRADY: *(Beat.)* He's not in this class.

SUBSTITUTE TEACHER: I'm sure Ms. DeSoto —

DALTON: It's Mrs.

SUBSTITUTE TEACHER: I'm sure *Mrs.* DeSoto will get the results to Jeremy when she's back.

(There's a long and terribly awkward silence. A barely stifled giggle comes from somewhere in the back.)

SABRINA: Not cool.

GIGGLING GIRL: Sorry...I'm not like laughing at him.

(Mario's lines for the rest of the scene are to himself, and the others should continue their conversation almost as if he's not there.)

MARIO: Don't say something stupid.

SABRINA: Then why are you laughing?

GIGGLING GIRL: I'm not. This is just like super freaky.

CHUCK: Your laugh is super freaky.

MARIO: Don't say anything.

GIGGLING GIRL: I get nervous.

CHUCK: That laugh makes me nervous.

DALTON: I know, right?

MARIO: Don't talk.

SABRINA: It's not funny.

CHUCK: I'm still pissed at you.

MARIO: Don't talk.

GIGGLING GIRL: I'm not trying to laugh.

DALTON: Dude, what is your problem?

SABRINA: Then try harder not to.

CHUCK: You.

MARIO: Don't talk.

BRADY: Shut up! All of you—just—shut—up!

(He storms out, leaving the classroom silent in his wake. Beat. Legolas steps out of the scene, and draws the light. During Legolas' monologue, Alisa exits.)

LEGOLAS: Six years ago, my uncle moved from apartment 208 to apartment 103. Same building. And so they start sending his disability checks to 103, which is what you expect, right? And then suddenly 2 months ago they start going back to 208. Lucky it's in the same building, but what's up with that? *(Beat.)* People think I'm weird. I'm OK with that. Tiny Tim, the little gimpy kid from *Christmas Carol*, says maybe people will see him and feel better cause they're not him. I think I'm something like that kind of weird. But not crazy. Not like "we flew our own planes into the Towers" crazy. And I say that the check suddenly going to my uncle's old address, or Jeremy's old aptitude test coming back, that's not an accident. *(Beat.)* I just hope—I hope it makes things better.

(The lights dim on the classroom, where all freeze. The lights come up on a hallway, where Brady sits on the ground by a locker in the hall. Alisa finds him.)

ALISA: I'm "in the bathroom."

BRADY: What's wrong with me?

ALISA: Can I get back to you on that?

(*Alisa sits next to him.*)

BRADY: (*Beat.*) I barely know you.

ALISA: What—you wanna blow your stranger danger whistle?

BRADY: No. Not that. I just shouldn't dump all this stuff on you.

ALISA: It's OK. Dump away.

BRADY: I can't.

ALISA: (*Beat.*) What if I dump first?

BRADY: And then I do?

ALISA: A dump for a dump. If you want. (*Beat.*) You don't have to decide now. (*Beat.*) I told you I have this shrine by my locker.

BRADY: Beth. It's a shrine to Beth.

ALISA: Who's dead.

BRADY: Who's dead.

ALISA: And I told you how I can barely get my books.

(*Brady nods.*)

I try to move it one tiny bit, and it's like they can smell that something moved, these three—

BRADY: The M Squad.

ALISA: The what?

BRADY: Popular, more popular and most popular.

ALISA: Great. First week and I'm screwed.

BRADY: Buy a T-shirt.

ALISA: A T-shirt...?

BRADY: It's like an offering.

ALISA: A what? I'm so confused right now.

BRADY: Wish you could take that dump back?

ALISA: Wish I could take back the word dump.

BRADY: They're like the gods — goddesses of popularity. You buy a shirt, it's like sacrificing a goat.

ALISA: Brady, you're so weird.

BRADY: Good weird?

ALISA: Weird.

BRADY: Thanks.

ALISA: *(Beat.)* What kind of T-shirt?

BRADY: The newest one's the all-black. But they have pretty much all of the good colors.

ALISA: Great.

BRADY: Fifteen dollars is cheap not to be the goat.

ALISA: Fifteen dollars doesn't solve the problem.

BRADY: Does for now. *(Beat.)* You should probably get back.

ALISA: I'll say there was blood involved.

BRADY: TMI.

ALISA: Yeah. So much worse than sacrificing a goat.

BRADY: That was a metaphor.

ALISA: *(Beat.)* Your turn.

BRADY: For...?

ALISA: To dump.

BRADY: You're not done yet.

ALISA: You said it was solved for now. *(Beat.)* I'll dump more later. Or spill. Spill's a better word.

BRADY: You said if I wanted.

(*He gets up.*)

I don't.

(*He walks away, leaving her there as the lights dim on her.*)

SCENE 3

(ROXANNA, student council president, confronts Marne.)

ROXANNA: You can't coerce people.

MARNE: Who's coercing?

ROXANNA: Don't play.

MARNE: *(Beat.)* How's the luau coming?

ROXANNA: Fine, but we're still talk—

MARNE: You get those tiki torches you wanted so bad?

ROXANNA: Yes, thank you.   *(Beat.)* We all felt...in the long run that buying them—I know it's more money upfront—but that way, if we do a Caribbean night or Polynesian—

(The lights shift as Marne steps out of this conversation. Roxanna stays frozen in place. Enter a quartet of NEEDY STUDENTS, who accost Marne in turn.)

FIRST STUDENT: Hey Marne.   Car wash came up a little short.

MARNE: Your signs kinda sucked. *(Beat.)* How short?

SECOND STUDENT: Two hundred if we want the good swing set.

FIRST STUDENT: It's rated safer.

THIRD STUDENT: Marne, you gotta sec?

FOURTH STUDENT: Hey Marne.

THIRD STUDENT: I know I said 250 was gonna be enough—

FOURTH STUDENT: I know you're probably sick of people asking—

THIRD STUDENT: —but if we don't bump up the shipping—

FOURTH STUDENT: —but is there any way to get another 300?

THIRD STUDENT: —it might not get here in time.

MARNE: *(To the Third Student:)* How much?

FOURTH STUDENT: Or else they're gonna have to share books.

MARNE: How much?

(Marne steps toward the First and Second Students.)

FIRST STUDENT: It'll last way longer, it's way more solid—

SECOND STUDENT: *(Holding up a brochure:)* Here—we brought it so you could see.

(Additional cast members could enter, or the original four students could be the chorus. Feel free to overlap or repeat some of the lines below:)

CHORUS OF STUDENTS: Marne, could you ?
Marne, can you—
Hey, Marne—
Marne, hey—
Marne?
Marne!

(Marne holds up her hand, silencing the crowd.)

MARNE: *(Walking away from them:)* Put Beth's name somewhere big.

(Marne steps out of their conversation and back into the conversation with Roxanna.)

ROXANNA: I'm just saying don't make it so obvious.

MARNE: I'm sorry. What are we talking about?

ROXANNA: In the caff—Chuck.

MARNE: No, we're not.

ROXANNA: I'm sorry. What?

MARNE: I'm sorry. Did your brains get sucked into that glossy little college portfolio you wave around like a magic wand? Because you are not getting the memo, and this is the last time we will be having this conversation. Without me and Beth Turner, your student council budget is the size of a chicken nugget; nobody's buying playground equipment for South Elementary or fixing the Adams Middle School trophy case, and they sure as hell aren't buying any torches to stick in the ground, no matter how many times you can reuse them.

ROXANNA: You know how much we appreciate—

MARNE: No. If I ever hear another word, you're cut off. We'll set up a freakin' scholarship fund for orphans in Africa, and I know nobody wants that.

> *(Marne stalks off, leaving Roxanna standing there wondering what hit her.)*

SCENE 4

(Alisa is in the office, which might just be indicated by a counter and a few chairs for those who wait. A SECRETARY wearing a mask, as do all of the adults in the play, busies herself doing who knows what.)

ALISA: Hi. Who do I —

SECRETARY: Be with you in a moment.

(Enter Buy Boy, not looking thrilled to be there — until he sees Alisa.)

BUY BOY: Hey you.

ALISA: Hi.

SECRETARY: Tanner, have a seat. You're at the top of Dr. Copperfield's list.

ALISA: Could I just ask —

BUY BOY: Is he —

SECRETARY: Oh yes.

BUY BOY: *(Under his breath:)* Great.

ALISA: I just have one really quick —

SECRETARY: Almost with you. I'm all alone today.

BUY BOY: What do you need?

ALISA: I want to change lockers.

(Enter DR. COPPERFIELD, masked.)

BUY BOY: Smart. I can hook you up.

DR. COPPERFIELD: Tanner, haven't you had enough hook-ups for one week?

BUY BOY: Dr. C, no — I just meant I'm helping my friend. Not that I did anything wrong before.

DR. COPPERFIELD: You can tell me all about it.

BUY BOY: *(To the Secretary as he gets sucked toward Copperfield's office:)* My friend Alisa needs a new locker, and I would totally see it as a personal favor if you could help her out.

(Buy Boy and Dr. Copperfield are gone. Beat.)

SECRETARY: What's your current locker?

ALISA: 842. It's near this, uh...

SECRETARY: The shrine?

(Alisa nods.)

Let me see what's open.

ALISA: Do I need to fill out any kind of change form, or...

(Beat. The PHONE RINGS.)

SECRETARY: *(Into the phone:)* Washington High School...

(Enter Headline.)

HEADLINE: Beautiful Girl Waits in the Office. And Waits. And Waits.

ALISA: Don't you have a class? *(Beat.)* I am not beautiful.

SECRETARY: OK. Lockers.

(Enter a TEACHER, also masked.)

TEACHER: Lois, is there any way you can help me out?

HEADLINE: Beautiful Girl Pushed to the Back of the Line Again.

ALISA: You are just slightly creepy —

(But she finds herself talking to the Secretary:)

Sorry. *(Points at Headline:)* Him. Not you.

SECRETARY: Unfortunately, there aren't any free lockers.

HEADLINE: Beautiful Girl Assigned to Locker in the Sophomore Hallway.

SECRETARY: There aren't any anywhere.

ALISA: There's not one locker in the whole school.

SECRETARY: Everything's assigned.

ALISA: If I can find someone to switch with me—

SECRETARY: Would you like to make an appointment with Dr. Copperfield?

HEADLINE: Beautiful Girl Fights Hopeless Fight.

ALISA: *(To Headline:)* Stop talking like that. Do you have any idea how irritating that is? *(Beat. To the Secretary:)* No. I'm fine.

SECRETARY: You let us know if there's anything we can do for you.

(Alisa walks out of the office, with Headline following her.)

HEADLINE: Fearless Reporter Apologizes.

ALISA: You're not a reporter.

(He continues to walk with her.)

I don't know what your malfunction is, but could you please just leave me alone?

(She continues walking, leaving him standing there.)

HEADLINE: Fearless Reporter Apolo—Hero Vows—Knight—Prince— *(Hitting himself in the head as the lights dim:)* Freak. Freak. Freak. Freak.

(Blackout.)

SCENE 5

(HYACINTH KROY, high school TV news reporter and the heir to Brady's spot, is live on camera. This could be done live or as a video projection.)

HYACINTH: This is Hyacinth Kroy with your Washington Warrior News. I know I don't need to tell you what Friday is, and I know that the entire Washington community will be there to show that one year later, Beth is still alive in our hearts. *(Beat.)* My guest at this time is QE Turner. QE, thank you for talking with us.

QE: Anything for Beth.

HYACINTH: Can you believe it's been a year?

QE: It has been.

HYACINTH: How is life different for you now?

QE: Well, things are a little better than right after it happened.

HYACINTH: Of course. Time heals, right?

QE: I guess.

HYACINTH: What can we expect tomorrow night?

QE: I dunno. Marne's organizing the whole thing. *(Beat.)* I'm saying a few words.

HYACINTH: What's it going to be like looking out into that sea of all black?

QE: I guess it'll be pretty amazing.

HYACINTH: *(Waving an all-black shirt:)* I've got mine right here. *(Beat.)* I think Beth would have been pretty stoked.

QE: Yeah. She always liked pep rallies. Guess this is kinda the same idea.

HYACINTH: I know your sister would be really proud of you.

QE: *(Beat.)* For what?

HYACINTH: Well, for being here. For everything you've been doing.

QE: I show up.

HYACINTH: You're representing.

QE: Am I?

(QE steps out of the scene.)

I didn't actually say that. Instead, it was this:

(QE steps back into the scene.)

HYACINTH: I know your sister would be really proud of you.

QE: Thanks. Our whole family was really proud of her. We always will be.

HYACINTH: She may be gone, but definitely not forgotten.

QE: Tomorrow's going to be an amazing day.

(The lights brighten around the stage to reveal other students.)

CHORUS OF STUDENTS: Is this on?
Friday night is about coming together.
I own all the shirts they ever put out.
Not like Beth's gonna care if I'm wearing a T-shirt with her face on it or reading a poem or telling a story about her life. It's for a good cause.
I knew Beth since elementary. Least I can do is show up.
You show up for everybody else. You show up for QE and Mr. and Mrs. Turner and all the people who were close to her. What if it was me, right?
I made varsity this year. Beth would have been captain.
I didn't know Beth, but I'm in trig with QE. Hate that class.

I'd want somebody to hug my mom.

FIRST CHORUS KID: Anybody know if there's an after party?

SECOND CHORUS KID: Like a wake?

FIRST CHORUS KID: I just wanna drink.

SECOND CHORUS KID: Dude, you are so inappropriate.

FIRST CHORUS KID: News is gonna be there. Maybe we'll get on TV.

SECOND CHORUS KID: Maybe you need to think about your life.

FIRST CHORUS KID: I think my life is awesome. Sometimes.

SECOND CHORUS KID: Instant karma's gonna get you.

FIRST CHORUS KID: Way to be original.

SECOND CHORUS KID: Old but true.

FIRST CHORUS KID: Whatever. See you at the vigil?

SECOND CHORUS KID: Dude, I'll see you next period. But yeah.

CAR KID: My car is 16 years old. That's like 112 in dog years. I think every part in the original car is gone. Mostly the new parts get along, but it's like when you have an organ donation, sometimes the body rejects the new organ. The lock on the driver's side door is having rejection issues.

WENDY: I don't like the lacrosse players. They didn't do anything to me, nothing like that. Just sometimes they're jerks. *(Beat.)* So you're probably thinking, "Why is she going to this thing for a lacrosse player?"

CAR KID: After two weeks of beautiful, perfect operation, the kind of love my classmates with Beamers, Toyotas and other fine German and Japanese vehicles take for granted, I'm sleeping on the couch—a.k.a. going in the passenger door, crawling over the gear shift—thank god I haven't slipped on that...much. I guess it's better than not having a car at all.

WENDY: But it's way bigger than that. It's like Beth brought us all together.

CAR KID: I've tried all the easy solutions, like WD40 and getting the key recut...and of course the place that sold it to me says there's nothing wrong with the lock. *(Beat.)* I have to take the door apart. But between school and my crap job serving food I wouldn't feed a dog I was trying to kill, I have no time. That's not true. I have Friday night. But I don't. Because I have to be at the vigil wearing the all-black that means I can't afford the part I need for another week.

WENDY: Tomorrow night when we're all in black T-shirts we're gonna be one school. I didn't want somebody to die for that, but it's good that it happened. I mean, it's good that this came out of it.

(End of scene.)

SCENE 6

(A school conference room. Marne, Melissa and Miranda count money. A few all-blacks are scattered about the room.)

MELISSA: Thirty-one, thirty-two, thirty-three, thirty-four, thirty-five, thirty-six—

MIRANDA: Do you seriously need to count out loud?

MELISSA: Do you want me to remember the count?

MARNE: Let's just get one of those Square [or payment processing tool of the moment] thingies.

MIRANDA: Good call.

MELISSA: Yeah—we all have smart phones.

MIRANDA: *(Under her breath:)* Smart phone, dumb user.

MELISSA: What?

MIRANDA: Nada.

MARNE: *(Finishing her count:)* It's official. The all-blacks are our biggest seller.

MELISSA: We should go out to dinner and celebrate.

MARNE: It's not about us.

MELISSA: Doesn't mean we can't celebrate our success. And not some ick fast food place.

MARNE: You know I don't eat fast food. Or chains.

MELISSA: So let the fund take us for Italian.

MARNE: The fund?

MIRANDA: *(Sotto to Marne:)* Somebody's been reading.

MELISSA: *(Ignoring Miranda:)* Well, we're like a charity—right?

MARNE: Yeah...?

MELISSA: Just cause it's a charity doesn't mean all the charity goes to charity.

MIRANDA: Cause *that* made sense.

MELISSA: Charities have overhead.

MIRANDA: Again with the big words.

MELISSA: Jealous much?

MIRANDA: Not much.

MELISSA: How much have we raised?

MIRANDA: Thousands.

MELISSA: And we can't get one lousy meatball dinner?

MIRANDA: I don't eat meatballs.

MELISSA: It was an example.

MIRANDA: I don't eat meat.

MELISSA: So have fish.

MIRANDA: I'm a vegan.

MELISSA: So have cheese ravioli. Who cares? The point is we've rocked Washington for a year. All-black sales are record-setting— *(To Marne:)* you said so yourself. *(To both:)* It's vigil eve. Nobody's gonna hate us for celebrating.

MIRANDA: Before we get all hallelujah, I got three no's on the all-black.

MARNE: No, as in—

MIRANDA: As in not buying—wait—four. The new girl.

MARNE: And the other three?

MIRANDA: You know which three.

MARNE: Cut them some slack.

MIRANDA: You've cut them plenty of slack.

MARNE: Maybe they deserve it.

MELISSA: *(Picking up Miranda's theme:)* Yeah, you've given them lots of chances.

MIRANDA: But people could say you've given them too many. *(Beat.)* If they don't buy, how long before it's 20 people, or 100, or until Beth is just a plaque on the wall that nobody sees in a hallway nobody even walks through? *(To Marne:)* And til you're just another ex-lacrosse player who used to matter...

MARNE: Don't forget why we do this.

MIRANDA: Why do we do this? Melissa, do you know?

MELISSA: I didn't even know her that well.

MIRANDA: Did you, Marne? You tore your whatever before the season even started. You didn't play a game with—

MARNE: Do you know how much I've done—

MIRANDA: I do. But people could start to forget that. I'm over my outfit five minutes after I put it on.

MELISSA: You too?

MARNE: Shut up, Melissa.

MIRANDA: *(To herself:)* Finally.

MELISSA: Uh, don't tell me to shut up.

MARNE: Then don't talk.

MIRANDA: *That's* what I'm talking about.

MELISSA: Why are you ganging up on me?

MARNE: Deal with it.

MELISSA: Hey! I'm just as in this as you.

MIRANDA: *(Ignoring Melissa:)* You are a world-class bitch, which is totally what I love about you.

MELISSA: So you can't tell me to shut up.

MARNE AND MIRANDA: Shut up!

MIRANDA: I just don't get why you suddenly turn all soft for these three losers.

   (Long pause.)

MARNE: Because we weren't the only ones who lost something.

MIRANDA: But who's got something to lose now? *(Beat.)* People want this. Look at what it's done for our school, for the whole community.

MARNE: Yeah, but isn't this why it happened in the first place?

MIRANDA: Beth got into an accident.

MARNE: I'm not talking about Beth.

MIRANDA: *(Beat.)* If you don't step up, somebody will.

   (Long pause.)

MARNE: I'm not there when it happens, and I don't know anything about it.

MELISSA: *(Beat.)* So...this celebration dinner...are we on?

   (The lights dim on them and come up on a hallway, where QE encounters VANESSA, a senior and Beth's best friend.)

QE: Hey.

VANESSA: Hey.

QE: Haven't seen you.

VANESSA: I thought second semester senior year was supposed to be like all parties and cruisin and...

QE: My parents asked if I'd talked to you.

VANESSA: I should come over more.

QE: It's cool.

VANESSA: I'm not avoiding you.

QE: I know.

VANESSA: Every time I go over, I keep expecting she's gonna come through the kitchen door and sit down in her spot and then say, "Look, Elvis!" and steal the pickles out of my sandwich.

QE: Yeah, you'd do that—

(QE and Vanessa make an elaborate show of looking away.)

VANESSA: —and she'd go swoop and—

QE: It's amazing how the sandwich was like it never had pickles on it at all.

VANESSA: Magic.

(Silence.)

QE: Why didn't you say something?

VANESSA: What?

QE: Why didn't you tell them no? They would have listened to you.

VANESSA: They would have listened to you too.

QE: I was only a freshman.

VANESSA: You were her sister.

QE: I still am. Did you stop being her best friend just 'cause she died?

VANESSA: I don't want to get into it with you, QE.

QE: Maybe we need to.

VANESSA: I wasn't here—remember?   Remember how it messed me up so bad I didn't get out of bed for three weeks? When I came back, it was done. The shrine was up, pens with her name on them were in every hand, the T-shirts were ordered, and the first vigil was already wrapped. *(Beat.)* If you hated it so much, why didn't you stop it? Why didn't your mom or your dad?

QE: The vigils are the only thing that keeps them together. If it wasn't for third Friday of every month, they wouldn't even talk to each other. *(Beat.)* The night Beth passed, my mom threw a coffee mug at my dad's head. She missed, but it was half full. We had to get the rug steam-cleaned. I was in my room with the door shut—they were making so much noise. I didn't hear Beth leave. I guess she saw the light in my window, 'cause I hear these horn taps outside.

VANESSA: Two taps, pause, one tap.

QE: And that was how we said goodbye forever.

(They sit on a bench in the hallway.)

VANESSA: Sorry.

QE: Me too. *(Beat.)* I just don't know what to do.

VANESSA: I was a way better athlete than Beth. OK—maybe not way better, but I bet if you asked her, she'd tell you I was

better—stronger, faster, whatever. But she was a better player.
It's like she was always in the right place, and the ball would
just end up on her stick. You know. You saw us play a zillion
times.

QE: A zillion and one.

VANESSA: It was just...

QE: Magic.

(Vanessa nods. They share a moment.)

VANESSA: She said it was all about the feel. Like somehow
she'd just feel the flow and know where to go, know what to
do. I think you'll feel it.

QE: You'll be there tomorrow—right?

*(QE takes Vanessa's hand, and together they sit in silence as the
lights fade on them and come up on Melissa, talking to a member
of the ensemble or someone we don't see. Melissa eats from a bag
of nachos [this could be another packaged bag of junk food].)*

MELISSA: Did I say lobster? No. Steak? Nope. I mean like
lobster ravioli would be nice, but I would have been totally
good with cheese. Actually, probably not pasta 'cause I'm
counting carbs but like whatever. But no. That would
actually require listening to me, and *(Sending up Marne and
Miranda:)* "we're M&M. We're way too busy thinking about
how awesome we are to listen to people who are really way
more awesome than us and who just want one meal to
celebrate that awesomeness instead of eating stupid vending
machine nachos filled with preservatives and artificial flavors
and yellow dye #6 and bitching to some random loser." No
offense. Tell anyone and you're dead. No—you'll just wish
you were. *(Holding out a nacho:)* Nacho?

(The lights dim on Melissa and come up on Alisa in the office,

trying to get the attention of the Secretary from before. As before, the adults wear masks.)

ALISA: Hi. It's me again. You said if there was anything you could do—

SECRETARY: Yes—may I help you?

ALISA: Yes.

SECRETARY: Yes?

ALISA: You can help me.

SECRETARY: Just a moment, please.

ALISA: But—

SECRETARY: Wait for it...

(Alisa is about to speak, but the Secretary holds up a finger to stop her. They wait. The PHONE RINGS.)

Washington High School...   Yes...   Yes...   Yes...   Uh—huh... Uh-huh...   Yes...   [etc.]

(Alisa moves closer, suspicious.)

Yes...   Uh-huh...   Yes...   [etc.]

ALISA: Is there anyone on the other end?

SECRETARY: Shhh...

ALISA: But you're not talking to anyone.

SECRETARY: I'll be with you in a jiffy.

ALISA: But I just—

SECRETARY: Oh no you don't.

ALISA: But—

SECRETARY: *(Covering her ears:)* Na na na na...   [etc.]

(Enter Dr. Copperfield.)

ALISA: Dr. Copperfield.

DR. COPPERFIELD: Sorry about that. Mrs. Ignora gets a little agitated sometimes.

(He keeps walking, heading "out" of the office. Alisa walks with him.)

ALISA: Could I just talk to—

DR. COPPERFIELD: I'm off to a meeting, but I would love to sit down and talk soon about whatever's on your mind.

ALISA: Can I walk you to your meeting?

DR. COPPERFIELD: You mean "may I."

ALISA: Yes.

DR. COPPERFIELD: I'll be walking extra quickly.

ALISA: I'll talk extra quickly.

DR. COPPERFIELD: It's not too late to make an appointment with Mrs. Ignora and avoid an uncomfortable situation.

ALISA: The shrine.

DR. COPPERFIELD: I'm going to walk faster now.

ALISA: Why can't it move just a little?

DR. COPPERFIELD: New student, aren't you?

ALISA: I can't get to my books.

DR. COPPERFIELD: Welcome to Washington High School.

ALISA: Thank you. But how am I supposed to get into my locker?

DR. COPPERFIELD: Let's see if there's another locker—

ALISA: There isn't any.

DR. COPPERFIELD: Maybe we can find one.

ALISA: Look—I know maybe I don't—

DR. COPPERFIELD: I'm almost at my meeting.

ALISA: Maybe I don't understand everything here, and not to sound like I don't care, but I'm pretty sure it's a fire hazard and it's not fair to give me a locker that I can't use or to switch me and make somebody else suffer instead, and this can't be the only student at Washington that's ever died.

DR. COPPERFIELD: *(Beat.)* We don't talk about that.

ALISA: Where are their shrines?

DR. COPPERFIELD: I'm at my meeting.

ALISA: But—

DR. COPPERFIELD: Your time is up.

(He walks into an imaginary room through an imaginary door, leaving Alisa standing alone. The lights dim on her as they come up on Luna, standing in a spotlight.)

LUNA: So when a planet gets demoted, what about its moons? One second, they're all planetary and sexy, and the next they're little chunks of rock orbiting some slightly bigger chunk of rock. *(Beat.)* It's like this woman in my neighborhood whose dad was a big general in communist Romania. One day she's growing up on easy street with the nicest toys and the best schools and dance lessons and caviar...and then he writes this novel that makes fun of the government and boom, hello prison for daddy and goodbye everything for the family. Not a good day to be a moon, the day that planet fell out of orbit. *(Beat.)* But after it happened, they didn't all burst into flames or fall apart into nothing. They kept right on going, as if everything was exactly the same. As if Pluto was every bit what it once was. As if he was right there at the table, eating a cheeseburger hold the cheese every Wednesday. And sometimes that's harder than hell, because all around you, you get the sense that everyone wishes you'd just disintegrate, because it would be easier to forget what happened here. But sooner or later everyone's gotta face it. We're going to have to answer for our crimes against Pluto.

SCENE 7

(Miranda and Chuck, the latter up against the wall, in some high school nook.)

CHUCK: I bought the all-black like you wanted. I don't have any more —

MIRANDA: You're not in trouble.

(Chuck lets out a sigh of relief.)

You like Marne, don't you?

CHUCK: Uh...no. Not, uh...like. You mean like like or —

MIRANDA: Don't lie.

CHUCK: Yes.

MIRANDA: Awww...that's so sweet.

CHUCK: If you're just gonna make fun of —

MIRANDA: Who's making fun of you? I just said it's sweet.

CHUCK: I guess.

MIRANDA: Did I or did I not just say it was sweet?

CHUCK: *(Beat.)* You've never talked to me before.

MIRANDA: That's not true.

CHUCK: You talk to me when you want something.

MIRANDA: Better than not talking to you at all.

CHUCK: So what do you want?

MIRANDA: Chuckie. Chuckie Chuck Chuck. Chuckety Chuckety. I like that. Chuckety Chuckety.

CHUCK: Great.

MIRANDA: So you like Marne, huh?

CHUCK: You asked me that already.

MIRANDA: Just making sure.

(Chuck nods. Long pause.)

You seem really nervous. Do I make you nervous?

CHUCK: If I'm about to get totally hosed, can we just get it over with?

MIRANDA: It must suck to hang out with a hottie like Dalton. Watch all those girls checking him out and know that they're not looking at you at all.

CHUCK: I bought what you wanted.

MIRANDA: Why does he hang out with you?

CHUCK: I did what you said.

MIRANDA: I just asked a question.

CHUCK: Our moms went to junior high together.

MIRANDA: That's cute.

CHUCK: I gotta go.

MIRANDA: No you don't.

CHUCK: But I—

MIRANDA: Maybe somebody's looking at you too... *(Beat.)* Marne needs your help.

CHUCK: *(Beat.)* She said that?

MIRANDA: She has this problem. And I'm sure if somebody solved it...

(She runs a finger up his chest.)

Imagine Marne doing that.

CHUCK: Oh God.

MIRANDA: Do you still have to go?

CHUCK: *(Barely audible:)* No.

MIRANDA: Just solve this problem...for Marne. I'm sure she'd be grateful. Especially now that she broke up with what's his name.

CHUCK: I didn't know they broke up.

MIRANDA: She doesn't want it to distract people before the vigil. *(Beat.)* They're still friends. *(Blowing in his ear or something similarly seductive:)* Just friends.

CHUCK: What's the problem?

(Lights dim on them as she whispers into his ear.)

SCENE 8

(LOU, short for Louise, has a box of T-shirts at her feet as Students pass by. A few buy shirts. A few already wear them.)

LOU: Last chance for the all-blacks before the vigil. Do not be left out. It will not be pretty. *(Beat.)* Got one already? Never hurts to have a twin. *(Beat.)* Got ten? Eleven's your lucky number.

(Alisa stops in front of Lou.)

How many you want?

ALISA: Just one, I think. *(Beat.)* Where's Marne?

LOU: She can't just stand around and sell T-shirts every day.

ALISA: But you're like an official salesperson or whatever.

LOU: Sorry—I forgot my name tag today.

ALISA: Sarcastic much?

LOU: Do I care much?

ALISA: OK. Dialing down the meowfest. I'd like to buy a shirt.

LOU: Cool. That's 15 dollars.

ALISA: *(Gives her money:)* So does Marne come by...

LOU: What are you like her wanna-be lesbian lover?

ALISA: *I'm* not selling her T-shirts.

LOU: They're Beth's T-shirts. Not like Marne's the only person who knew her.

ALISA: *(Beat.)* She was cool?

LOU: For realz. I was on the talent show committee and she was like co-head producer of the whole thing, but she knew everybody's name and she'd bring donuts and talk to the underclassmen and stuff. Like "how was your day," that kind of thing, but you could tell she was actually listening to the answer.

ALISA: She sounds cool. *(Beat.)* So can you just make sure Marne knows I bought one?

LOU: Hey, I totally support your sexual preference.

ALISA: I'm not —

LOU: It's all good.

ALISA: I'm not a lesbian.

LOU: Not judging.

ALISA: I just think it's better if she knows I bought one.

LOU: *(Beat.)* For realz.

(Alisa walks away as Brady emerges. He's been watching.)

ALISA: Are you spying on me?

BRADY: You did the right thing.

ALISA: I'm not talking to you.

LOU: *(To herself:)* I take it back. Not a lesbian. *(Louder:)* Later, Romeo and Juliet.

ALISA: We agreed. I dump, you dump. But then you left me standing there. Sitting there.

BRADY: You don't understand.

ALISA: I'm not talking to you.

BRADY: You're talking to me right now.

ALISA: *(Walking away:)* Not anymore.

BRADY: You don't know what happened.

ALISA: Beth died. I get it.

BRADY: No. Jeremy died.

ALISA: Who's — *(Beat.)* He's the name in math class. The day we had the substitute.

BRADY: He died two weeks before Beth. Not even two weeks. A week and a half. They say he hung himself in his garage, but I don't even know if that's how he did it, because nobody ever talks about it.

(A long silence.)

ALISA: He was your friend?

BRADY: I don't know. *(Beat.)* I was in a couple of classes with him. We were lab partners in bio twice. *(Beat.)* But I don't think it matters, you know. He was somebody we knew, and then he was gone and 10 days later everybody had a better story to hold onto.

(The lights change to indicate that we've moved outside of real time. Enter the masked Dr. Copperfield and a masked chorus of ADULTS. Brady steps into the scene.)

DR. COPPERFIELD: At this time, Jeremy Reiner's family has asked that you respect their privacy.

MASKED CHORUS MEMBERS: We don't want to give students ideas.
We don't want to glorify it.

BRADY: Is talking about it glorifying it?

DR. COPPERFIELD: Talking about it is against the family's wishes.

MASKED CHORUS MEMBERS: Haven't they been through enough?

(To another Masked Chorus Member:) Do you want something to come out?

People are litigious.

We didn't do anything wrong.

What if we did?

> *(Enter Hyacinth and DANIELLE, the student TV producer, as the stylized scene continues.)*

BRADY: This is exactly what we should be covering.

HYACINTH: They've already told us no.

BRADY: Hello, First Amendment.

DANIELLE: Doesn't always fully apply in schools.

BRADY: Since when?

DANIELLE: You know—shocker—there was a TV station before you got here. Two years ago I was you, and the producer laid down the law. Literally.

BRADY: We're supposed to be journalists. How can we be if we don't report on the things that are real?

HYACINTH: The family doesn't want us to report on it.

BRADY: Why is she even here?

DANIELLE: I asked her to come.

BRADY: People need to know what happened.

DANIELLE: They know. But sometimes other things come first.

BRADY: Like what? *(Beat.)* Did you ever think maybe if we covered it, it would help?

DANIELLE: How would covering it help anyone? It would just make people sad and confused.

BRADY: Like he was?

DANIELLE: We don't know that.

BRADY: Oh, so people kill themselves because they're happy now.

HYACINTH: We don't know why he did it.

BRADY: Really not looking for your input.

DANIELLE: Either way, he's gone and the rest of us are still here. We have to go on.

BRADY: What if there's somebody else just like him? What if talking about it could be the one thing that—

DANIELLE: When you get a cut, a really bad one, the last thing you do is pour salt in it.

BRADY: But what if there's something we could change?

DANIELLE: *(Beat.)* Start with yourself. That's all we can really control.

BRADY: I don't accept that.

DANIELLE: Sorry. You kinda have to. *(Beat.)* Brady, you're my ace reporter on the scene—

BRADY: Who never covers anything important.

DANIELLE: If you want to *stay* my ace reporter...

BRADY: *(To Hyacinth:)* If I go all rogue, do you get my job? *(Beat.)* Let me guess: another school board meeting, or is the baseball team saving the animal shelter yet again with a car wash?

(The others leave, the lights shift back, and Brady is left alone with Alisa.)

I get Beth. Accidents happen. They suck, but bad things

happen. Sometimes bad things happen to good people. Isn't that what they say? But Jeremy wasn't an accident, and maybe all I had to do was reach out one hand, and everything would be different.

ALISA: And I'm sure there's a dozen people or a dozen dozen that are thinking the same thing.

BRADY: Nobody even remembers him.

ALISA: How do you know?

BRADY: They never mention his name. When the sub read his name in class, that was the first time anybody said it practically since it happened.

ALISA: Maybe they don't know how. Maybe they want to, but they need help.

(Beat. Enter Hyacinth.)

HYACINTH: Getting the scoop for the-? Wait—you don't do that anymore.

BRADY: Isn't this the part where you pretend to be all nice in front of other people?

HYACINTH: *(Fake nice:)* Hyacinth Kroy from Washington Warrior News.

BRADY: I used to be her.

HYACINTH: You were never me.

BRADY: Yeah. My heart actually beats.

HYACINTH: Are you two, uh... He's charming in an unleash your inner goth kind of way. Speaking of which... *(Indicates the T-shirt:)* good fashion choice.

ALISA: Thank you. I'm—

BRADY: She doesn't care.

HYACINTH: So negative, Brady. *(To Alisa:)* He's been so negative since his little on-air meltdown.

BRADY: You would've—

HYACINTH: Done my job. All you had to do was hold it together for another 30 seconds and right now you'd be preparing to host the high school news special that's getting picked up live on network TV. They'd be beaming your face into living rooms all over NYC.

BRADY: *(Beat.)* Congratulations.

HYACINTH: Don't get me wrong. On a personal level, I'm stoked that you choked. Wow. I just rhymed. *(Beat.)* But as much as you think I'm all about leaving a trail of broken dreams on my way to the top, before I didn't like you, I kinda did. But I wasn't gonna not take the gig.

BRADY: And that meeting?

HYACINTH: Danielle told me to come. So I did.

(A long silence.)

BRADY: Network, huh?

HYACINTH: How a school came together in adversity and all that.

ALISA: Sounds inspiring.

HYACINTH: Feel good moment of the week. *(Beat.)* Gotta bounce.

ALISA: I'll be there in my all-black.

HYACINTH: That sea of all-blacks...gonna make for some great visuals.

BRADY: Hope it's amazing for you.

(Hyacinth turns to leave, then turns back. Beat.)

HYACINTH: *(To Brady:)* Hey—it's not on-camera, but Robby's got chicken pox or maybe Ebola. Probably not Ebola, but they're not letting him out of bed, which means we're one sound grunt down. I know you did that when you were a frosh.

BRADY: You're asking me to—

HYACINTH: Never mind. I shouldn't have—

BRADY: I'll do it. *(Beat.)* Maybe when it's over, put in a good word with Danielle?

HYACINTH: You're not getting my job.

BRADY: Sports'll be open when Carlos graduates. Or entertainment. *(As if he's on air:)* This is Brady Winters reporting live from the scene of Washington's latest sporting triumph.

HYACINTH: We'll see. Just make sure they can hear me.

BRADY: They'll get it loud and clear.

HYACINTH: *(To Alisa, approvingly:)* You and him a—

ALISA: No, we're not uh—

BRADY: No, uh. .

HYACINTH: *(To Alisa:)* Well, whatever you're doing...

    (Hyacinth exits.)

ALISA: TV station. That would be good for you, right?

BRADY: Sound guy.

ALISA: Gets your foot back in the door.

BRADY: *(Having an idea:)* And near the audio feed.

SCENE 9

(Friday morning. In the dark:)

ANNOUNCEMENT: Good morning, Washington High School. Welcome to your Friday. After school, Warrior baseball takes on Garden City at Garden City, and boys' lacrosse takes on Garden City here at home. Come out and root for your Warriors, and then stay, because we all know what tonight is. Right here on the lacrosse field —

(The announcement is punctuated by a HOWL. Lights up on Legolas, on his knees in front of his locker.)

LEGOLAS: It's all gone. It's all destroyed. It's all gone.

(He holds up his books and assorted other items in his locker. They're all black, as if they've been marinated in paint. Sabrina tries to console him.)

SABRINA: We'll fix this.

LEGOLAS: Everything's black. They painted it all black.

CHUCK: *(To Miranda:)* Guess he's got an all-black now.

SABRINA: It'll be OK.

LEGOLAS: *(Holding up a black-painted flash drive:)* Look at my flash drive.

SABRINA: We'll be OK.

LEGOLAS: My life was on my flash drive.

SABRINA: She'll give you an extension.

LEGOLAS: This *was* my extension.

SABRINA: *(To Marne:)* Are you happy? Are you happy now?

MARNE: What?

SABRINA: You know what.

MARNE: I didn't do anything.

HEADLINE: Student Victim of All-Black Attack.

SABRINA: It's a T-shirt.

LEGOLAS: I am so dead.

SABRINA: I know you did this.

MARNE: You need to chill out.

SABRINA: You are so dead.

MIRANDA: Did she just threaten you?

CHUCK: Dang — she's goin' mad dog.

SABRINA: You mess with me and I will kill you.

(Dalton steps between them to keep Sabrina from getting to Marne.)

DALTON: Whoa — everybody chill.

MIRANDA: She totally threatened you.

MARNE: *(To Sabrina:)* I didn't touch his stuff, and I didn't tell anybody to. *(To Legolas:)* I didn't touch your stuff.

MIRANDA: Don't even talk to her.

LEGOLAS: I'm gonna flunk out. My parents are gonna kill me.

SABRIINA: Don't talk like that.

LEGOLAS: I want to die. I want to die.

MIRANDA: Oh my god, I can't believe she threatened you.

DALTON: Totally over the line.

SABRINA: We'll talk to Dr. Copperfield...

LEGOLAS: I just want to not exist.

SABRINA: No you don't.

CHUCK: Psycho.

(Enter Dr. Copperfield, in a mask.)

MIRANDA: She used the words "I will kill you."

DR. COPPERFIELD: Sabrina, you'll need to come with me.

SABRINA: But she destroyed—

MIRANDA: Zero tolerance.

SABRINA: You shut up.

DR. COPPERFIELD: Sabrina! *(Beat. To Sabrina:)* I'm sorry.

MARNE: I had nothing to do with this.

DR. COPPERFIELD: *(To Sabrina:)* We'll need to call your parents.

MIRANDA: Zero tolerance.

SABRINA: *(Pointing at Marne:)* Call *her* parents. She's the one—

MARNE: Why would I jeopardize the vigil—

DR. COPPERFIELD: Sabrina. *(To the Students:)* Everyone, get to class.

(He escorts Sabrina, who looks ready to kill Marne and Miranda, offstage. The crowd breaks up, and the stage divides itself into four parts: Legolas, destroyed, sits amidst the ruins of his life, with Brady and Alisa on the fringe of his world, watching him; Chuck sidles up to Marne, with Miranda lurking nearby; Habit observes Legolas from the corner of the stage. Finally, Wendy and Pam rehearse a scene from the gender-bent production of Richard II. Other students might enter with them, bearing a coffin.)

CHUCK: I did that for you.

MARNE: Did what?

CHUCK: You know what.

WENDY: From Exton's entrance in Act Five, Scene Six.

BRADY: Hey. *(Beat.)* Are you OK?

LEGOLAS: *(Shaking his head, quietly:)* No.

BRADY: Can I help?

LEGOLAS: I don't know.

BRADY: Can I sit with you?

PAM: *(As Exton:)* Great king, within this coffin I present
The mightiest of thy greatest enemies,
Richard of Bordeaux.

MARNE: I didn't ask you to do this.

WENDY: *(As Bolingbroke:)* Exton, I thank thee not;

BRADY: This is Alisa.

    (Legolas doesn't look up.)

She's pretty.

    (Alisa registers Brady's remark before turning to Legolas.)

ALISA: Hi.

CHUCK: Miranda, tell her —

MIRANDA: Tell her what?

PAM: *(As Exton:)* From your own mouth, my lord, did I this deed.

WENDY: *(As Bolingbroke:)* They love not poison that do poison need,

Nor do I thee.

MARNE: You should go, Chuck.

WENDY: *(As Bolingbroke:)* With Cain go wander through shades of night,
And never show thy head by day nor light.

CHUCK: I—I'll see you later.

MARNE: That wouldn't be a good idea.

(Marne exits, with Miranda following. Beat. Chuck exits in a different direction.)

LEGOLAS: You don't have to stay with me.

ALISA: We know.

(Alisa and Brady continue to look after Legolas, but the lights dim on them and come up more fully on Habit.)

HABIT: I shouldn't be here. *(Beat.)* When my basketball coach died, back when I still played sports, back in sixth grade, I was the only player on the team who didn't go to the funeral. I had a piano lesson. My mom has the phone in her hand, and she's dialing my piano teacher, and I swear I almost grab it from her fingers. I didn't really do that, but I tell her no, I don't know if Mr. McCleary has any other times for my lesson. And my mom hangs up the phone, and that's that. *(Beat.)* And the day after the funeral, I hear them—all my teammates—talking about it and hugging, and I don't know what to say. I'm on the outside, and I will never again get back in. *(Beat.)* I want that night back. I want a do-over. I want to let my mom make that call. Maybe things would be different. Like in those movies when people go back in time, and they change one thing, and when they get home they live in a mansion instead of a one plus one apartment, and their parents are happy and never scream things like "I see how you look at her" or "you're such a bloodsucking bitch." I quit the piano six months later anyway. *(Beat. Pointing at Legolas:)* I should be there. But I just can't. I know if I take one step my insides will start to melt and my lungs will drown and I will end. I am not ready for the end of the world. Not yet.

(Beat. Habit exits.)

SCENE 10

(Alisa intercepts Buy Boy in the hall.)

ALISA: Hey.

BUY BOY: *(Looks around:)* Hey. Me?

ALISA: Yeah.

BUY BOY: Hey.

ALISA: You remember you said if I needed something...

BUY BOY: I got you covered.

ALISA: I need a shark.

BUY BOY: Shark... That's like a...what is that?

ALISA: It's a shark. *(Beat.)* It's a joke.

BUY BOY: I get it. You're messin' with me.

ALISA: I need a sound system.

BUY BOY: You messin' with—

ALISA: No. I really need one.

BUY BOY: Wanna make your car go thumpa thumpa boom?

ALISA: Something like that.

BUY BOY: I got you.

ALISA: I need it by tonight.

BUY BOY: Tonight. That's fast.

ALISA: That a problem?

BUY BOY: *(Beat.)* Like I said, I got you.

> *(She drifts away. Buy Boy contemplates her. As the lights dim on him, he pulls out a cell phone and dials as he exits. The lights come up on Brady and Mario.)*

MARIO: My whole family has their union cards. My dad, my gramps, his dad — how could that test say that I'm the only one not good enough for the union?

BRADY: Then show 'em.

MARIO: Show 'em what?

BRADY: That you're good enough.

MARIO: How'm I gonna do that?

BRADY: I know this job. Wiring job.

MARIO: What's it pay?

BRADY: The only guy who could do this job...only a union guy could do this job.

MARIO: Union pay?

(There's a long and awkward silence. Obviously, there's no pay.)

This is exactly how I get tossed out of the union.

BRADY: Mario, come on.

MARIO: This is a test, isn't it?

BRADY: No.

MARIO: I say yes, I'm screwed [doomed].

BRADY: I have nothing to do with that.

MARIO: My whole life is flashing in front of my eyes.

BRADY: Mario, I need your help. Tonight might be my one chance, and you're the only guy I know who can do this wiring. I need to make this right.

MARIO: Make what right?

BRADY: I think you know.

MARIO: *(Beat.)* Only one, huh?

(Brady nods.)

If a guy was the only one who could do a certain thing, a certain union kind of skill, they'd have to let him in.

BRADY: Total no-brainer.

MARIO: *(Beat.)* You ever tell anybody I worked for below scale...

(Brady makes a show of zipping his lips and throwing away the "key." He exits as the lights dim.)

SCENE 11

(A locker room. Enter Dalton. Chuck is there, his back turned. During the scene, Dalton gets changed from his school clothes into a lacrosse uniform.)

DALTON: Hey Douche, JV doesn't have a game today.

(Chuck says nothing.)

OK—so what do you think—would it be totally awkward to ask Miranda out tonight? After, obviously.

(Chuck shrugs. He's crying, but making sure Dalton can't see him.)

But like I'll see her and she hugs me and I hug her and she'll be all like I'm so glad you're here and I'll be like you know I'm here for you. I'll always be here for you. And she'll be like, I want to be with you. And I say, I don't want you to go through this alone. That's too much, isn't it? It sounds super weird when I say it out loud. I don't want her to think I had it all planned. I mean what kind of a douche asks somebody out at a memorial? Do you think she's coming to my game? If she comes to the game and we win I could ask her out after. That would be less weird.

(Chuck doesn't answer. He's trying to be as quiet as possible, but he can't quite hide the fact that he's sobbing.)

Dude, are you crying?

(Chuck shakes his head.)

You're totally crying.

CHUCK: I'm not. *(Beat.)* Can you just go?

DALTON: Are you still pissed about the shirt? Dude, I'll give you the 20 bucks.

CHUCK: Who cares about the stupid shirt?!

DALTON: Chill out.

CHUCK: I messed up. I messed up so bad.

DALTON: I'm sure it's not that bad.

CHUCK: It is.

DALTON: It'll be OK. Wait for me after the game. We'll go over together.

CHUCK: They don't want me there.

DALTON: Don't be stupid.

CHUCK: They don't. *(Beat.)* Why are you even friends with me?

DALTON: Stop talkin' like such a douche.

CHUCK: She told me to do it. She told me to —

DALTON: I don't want to know this.

CHUCK: You know.

DALTON: No.

CHUCK: Pretty soon, everyone's gonna know everything.

DALTON: Your mom still got that chocolate cake in the freezer, the one with the raspberries? Maybe after we can —

CHUCK: My dad's gonna tell me what a disappointment I am again —

DALTON: Got a six-pack with your name on it.

CHUCK: My mom doesn't even yell anymore.

DALTON: There's two with my name on 'em.

CHUCK: She just looks at me with this look, and her eyes, they're just so sad it feels like this hand is reaching into my chest and tearing my heart out —

DALTON: You'll be OK.

CHUCK: If I just disappeared, nobody'd even care. Why am I so dumb?

DALTON: Don't talk like that.

CHUCK: What am I gonna' do?

DALTON: *(Beat.)* Just come to the vigil.

CHUCK: I told you they don't want me there.

DALTON: Everybody's gonna be there.

CHUCK: How long do you think I got?

DALTON: What?

CHUCK: Til everybody finds out. Monday?

DALTON: You're gonna make yourself crazy.

CHUCK: Think I got the weekend? *(Beat.)* Maybe I could go to Mexico.

DALTON: You're not going to Mexico. *(Beat.)* Just come to the vigil tonight.

CHUCK: I am not a good person.

DALTON: *(Kindly:)* You're a douche.

(*The BELL RINGS. By this point, Dalton should be fully changed.*)

Promise you're not gonna do something stupid.

CHUCK: I always do stupid stuff.

DALTON: You know what I mean.

CHUCK: Why do you even care? *(Beat.)* OK.

(The lights dim on them and come up on Marne and Miranda. They're at Marne's locker.)

MIRANDA: The orchestra is sound checking at 6:15, the flowers should get delivered by 6:30 and honor society's got people coming to arrange them at 6:45 — the game is starting 30 minutes early to make sure it doesn't run over. News crew is supposed to set up by 7:00. The real news. Ours is gonna be there by 6 so they can get everything right and not make us look nationally stupid.

MARNE: OK.

MIRANDA: OK?

MARNE: Uh-huh.

MIRANDA: That's all?

MARNE: Do you want a medal?

MIRANDA: What's your deal?

MARNE: You know what my deal is.

MIRANDA: You said take care of it. What did you think was gonna happen?

MARNE: That's not what I meant.

MIRANDA: No? What did you mean?

MARNE: Not that.

(An invisible person passes by, and both Marne and Miranda don plastic smiles, watching the passerby disappear. Pause.)

MIRANDA: Maybe you should say what you mean next time.

MARNE: Why wait? *(Beat.)* You've wanted my spot since you wore my dress to my birthday party.

MIRANDA: It wasn't yours.

MARNE: It was an exact copy. *(Beat.)* My mom made me change, because it wasn't like we could send you home to get a new one.

MIRANDA: You're seriously talking about something that happened when we were nine?

MARNE: Maybe if you weren't a bitch and a half I wouldn't have to.

MIRANDA: Better than being half a bitch.

MARNE: That makes no sense.

MIRANDA: You make no sense. *(Beat.)* OK. Picture this. In front of you, you have three Twinkies.

MARNE: Why am I picturing Twinkies?

MIRANDA: Just picture them.

MARNE: Whatever. I like Twinkies.

MIRANDA: Then not Twinkies. Moldy apples.

MARNE: That's gross.

MIRANDA: And right behind them, there's like the most amazing dinner.

MARNE: What is it?

MIRANDA: I don't know. It's like the most amazing dinner ever, cooked by somebody really famous. And if you want it, all you have to do is throw away the apples.

MARNE: This is totally stupid.

MIRANDA: Life is stupid.

MARNE: True dat.

MIRANDA: True dat? You don't talk that way.

MARNE: *(Her mood lightening:)* I'm experimenting.

MIRANDA: *(Giggling:)* Experimenting? *(Beat.)* Think of how famous we're gonna be.

MARNE: It's not about that.

MIRANDA: Yeah, but think of how much bigger this could be. Like huge big. Like epic.

MARNE: National coverage is definitely epic. *(Beat.)* Can you imagine if somewhere on some random street in like...San Diego...they made a Beth Turner Memorial Park?

MIRANDA: That'd be sweet.

(They share a moment. Beat. Enter Melissa carrying a pair of dresses, one red and one black and wrapped in plastic, over her shoulder.)

MELISSA: OK. So all-black on red or all-black on black?

MARNE: Just as long as you don't wear what I'm wearing...

(They exit, as the lights dim on them and come up on...)

SCENE 12

(The lacrosse field. Shortly before the vigil. The masked TV Reporter from the opening scene, masked CAMERA MAN in tow, is there talking to Hyacinth. Enter Brady, in his all-black but otherwise looking like a sound guy.)

HEADLINE: Entire School Prepares for Vigil.

TV REPORTER: This is perfect. We'll set up here, so we'll have the whole crowd behind us.

HYACINTH: We. I can't tell you what an honor it is to work with you.

TV REPORTER: I think we're all honored to be able to share this good work with a larger audience.

BRADY: *(To Hyacinth:)* Excuse me — did you need me to do anything else for now?

HYACINTH: I think we're good.

(There's an awkward moment of Hyacinth not introducing Brady to the TV Reporter.)

TV REPORTER: Hi. Cyndi Jackson.

BRADY: Brady.

TV REPORTER: It's a pleasure to meet you, Brady. *(Beat.)* You look familiar.

HYACINTH: He's filling in on sound today.

TV REPORTER: I just feel like I've seen you somewhere.

BRADY: I'm just the sound grunt.

TV REPORTER: Then your job's as important as it gets. Without you, no one hears us at all.

HYACINTH: You checked everything?

BRADY: Good to go.

HYACINTH: Thank you.

BRADY: *(To Cynthia:)* It was good to meet you.

(The ensemble trickles onto the stage, entering and setting it for the vigil.)

QE: *(Practicing:)* Thank you all for coming.

VANESSA: *(Practicing:)* Thank you all for coming.

MARNE: *(Practicing:)* Thank you all for coming.

TV REPORTER: This is Cyndi Jackson, reporting live from Washington High School.

HYACINTH: This is Hyacinth Kroy with Washington Warrior News, and in a few moments —

TV REPORTER: —and in minutes, we'll be letting a high school broadcast—

HYACINTH: —we will be making history—

TV REPORTER: —rule our airwaves. Just as we'll be bringing our broadcasts together—

HYACINTH: —as the first high school news show to have its broadcast carried live by a major network affiliate.

TV REPORTER: —so has this school brought a community together in the face of a tremendous loss.

CHORUS OF STUDENTS: I've gotta charge my phone. You can't wave a dead phone in the air.
(Said by Car Kid:) Stop thinking about your car. Stop thinking about your car with the busted door.
I wish I could cry. Nobody thinks you care unless you cry.
If I cry, will they think I'm weak?
(Continuing until the next actor interrupts:) I'm on the beach. I'm

on the beach. I'm on the beach. I'm on the —
There's something really wrong here.
Don't cry. Everybody knows you didn't know her, and they'll
know it's fake.
Melissa didn't know her at all, and I'll bet she'll be hugging
everybody and crying like they were best friends.
I feel like we're about to be swallowed whole.

HEADLINE: School Gathers on Lacrosse Field at Dusk.

*(We hear CROWD SOUNDS. Lights come up on Brady and
Alisa, huddled in the corner, while the rest of the stage – and all
of the people on it – remains dimly lit.)*

BRADY: I think I'm gonna throw up.

ALISA: It's OK.

BRADY: What's OK about it?

ALISA: It will *be* OK.

BRADY: I told you I'm crap at bravery.

ALISA: You also said maybe people needed a little help. To
talk about it.

BRADY: *You* said that.

ALISA: *(Beat.)* Yeah. Guess that was me.

BRADY: It should have been me. *(Beat.)* I'm gonna get in so
much trouble.

(She takes his hand.)

I feel like a star's exploding and every light there ever was is
shining in my eyes.

ALISA: It'll be OK.

BRADY: I think it's because you're holding my hand. That
was so corny.

ALISA: The star or the holding my hand?

BRADY: Both.

ALISA: They were sweet.

BRADY: Yeah?

(He disappears into the shadows, and Alisa melts into the crowd. Lights come up on Marne standing at a podium, flanked by QE, Vanessa, Melissa and Miranda. As many other cast members as possible – feel free to use extras – should be in the crowd. Again, any adults should be masked. In a smallish cast production, one could imply the crowd through sound.)

MARNE: I get a chill every time I walk on this field. Did Beth step here? Or here? Did she score from here? *(Beat.)* I'm sure most of us who remember Beth go through that every day. And that's why we're here tonight. To remember. I think you all know me, Marne Warren, and I think you know Miranda Conway and Melissa Erickson.

MIRANDA: *(Leaning over Marne:)* Can I just say how amazing it is to see this sea of all black? It's like –

MARNE: We are all together. One heart.

(Hyacinth is in full TV reporter mode, perhaps downstage and off to the side. Marne and company mime speaking while Hyacinth reports. First Vanessa and then QE step up to speak. We hear occasional CHEERING and APPLAUSE from the crowd in the background as they pantomime their speeches.)

TV REPORTER: We are going to let the video and teen reporter Hyacinth Kroy of Washington Warrior News speak for us here at News 4.

HYACINTH: As QE, Beth's younger sister, has come up to the podium, I think there may be 500 cell phones in the air. It's the most incredible thing I've ever seen. It's like the entire crowd is acting as one person.

(*QE waves, and Marne returns to the podium.*)

MARNE: Thank you, QE, and thank you all for being part of something amazing. And I'm not talking about tonight, though tonight is pretty amazing. I'm talking about (*Referring to notes now:*) new playground equipment for South Elementary, books for an entire Adams Middle School classroom, and there's so much more to —

(*Lights up on Brady, broadcasting from inside the student TV station. He interrupts Marne, whose microphone cuts out. Brady preempts the entire broadcast.*)

BRADY: Hello? Hi.

MARNE: What the — ?

BRADY: QE, Vanessa, I'm really sorry.

MIRANDA: What the eff?

HYACINTH: (*To herself:*) Brady!?

BRADY: I didn't know Beth — I interviewed her once after she got named all-state and Carlos got food poisoning, but everybody always said she was a pretty awesome person. I'm sorry to ruin her night. It's just that there's something else we need to talk about, and I didn't know any other way to do it, so I hijacked the audio feed and locked myself inside the TV station.

HEADLINE: Student Takes Over Live TV Broadcast.

TV REPORTER: Keep rolling on this.

BRADY: Sorry, Hyacinth.

HYACINTH: You are so dead.

MARNE: Somebody get to the TV station!

MIRANDA: Dr. Copperfield!

BRADY: There was this kid who went to our school. His name was Jeremy. Jeremy Reiner. And he died. Maybe he hung himself in his garage. I don't know for sure, 'cause nobody ever talked about it. And we need to. *I* need to. Maybe it's just me in the whole school. If it is, I'm sorry for taking up your time with my problems.

DR. COPPERFIELD: Brady, come out of there.

BRADY: But if there's one other person out there that feels the same way...

> *(Beat. There's a BANGING on the TV station door. As the scene continues, the staging can become more and more stylized.)*

Jeremy was in 10th grade, a year younger than Beth, and way less popular, and he didn't do any clubs or sports. Or maybe he did and I didn't know.

DR. COPPERFIELD: Brady, open that door.

HEADLINE: Vigil Plunges Into Chaos.

MELISSA: He's messing up everything.

MIRANDA: Somebody unplug the sound system.

BRADY: But he went to our school and he was in two of my classes and in biology he wouldn't dissect a frog.

DR. COPPERFIELD: It won't be just a suspension, young man.

MIRANDA: *(To Hyacinth:)* How do we unplug the speakers?

BUY BOY: Damn—I'm like helping overthrow the government.

BRADY: I know a lot of people don't want to dissect frogs...

HEADLINE: Student Under Siege Stands Strong.

MIRANDA: Just cut him off.

BRADY: I guess that doesn't make him special.

MELISSA: Cut the power.

MARNE: Don't.

MIRANDA: Marne, I told you —

BRADY: But why do people have to be "special" just to be special?

VANESSA: Don't unplug it.

MELISSA: Vanessa, no offense —

MARNE: Don't unplug it.

BRADY: The day he died, I was supposed to invite him to dinner.

DR. COPPERFIELD: Brady, this is very serious.

MARNE: When I was in 4th grade, Jeremy was the first stop on bus 38.

MIRANDA: *(To Marne:)* What are you doing?

MARNE: I was the last stop. The bus was always full.

BRADY: He had this slide.

MIRANDA: You're gonna mess up everything.

MARNE: So I sat next to Jeremy for six minutes a day.

LEGOLAS: He called me. At 4:01 PM. I was playing some game, and my phone's buzzing on my desk and I can't reach it.

BRADY: This slide from the bio lab we did together.

LEGOLAS: Not without taking my hand off the joystick and losing a life.

MARNE: He tried to hold my hand once. Dalton and this girl Athena Campbell who doesn't even go to our school anymore were holding hands in the seat across from us, so Jeremy, he looks at me.

BRADY: One of those glass ones you put under a microscope.

LEGOLAS: Jeremy would always call like five times in a row if you didn't pick up. I figure he'll call any minute.

MARNE: It's like he's measuring the distance, and then he reaches. But at that exact second I have this itch, and I scratch my arm. It totally looks like I moved my hand on purpose.

BRADY: Why's he still carrying around a slide from three months ago?

LEGOLAS: 4:19, I call *him*. No answer. 4:23. 4:27, 4:40, 4:53. 5:00 PM. I want to go over, but it's too far to walk or bike, and nobody's home.

MARNE: I can see he's ready to cry. And I want to reach out and take his hand, but I don't.

BRADY: And I keep thinking this is weird and are other people hearing this?

LEGOLAS: But I run out the door and even though I am useless and ridiculous, I can't stop, because I just can't shake this feeling.

MARNE: If I'd just touched him once...

BRADY: I can't invite him to dinner if other people are hearing this.

LEGOLAS: This feeling that something is terribly, terribly wrong.

BRADY: Crap at bravery.

CHORUS OF STUDENTS: *(Each sentence a different student:)* You think about every little thing—'cause maybe it was giant and you just couldn't see it.

> *(Beat.)*

He'd try to start a conversation sometimes before homeroom, but I'd always say a word or two and then walk away.
I wasn't horrible to him, but I wasn't nice to him.

HABIT: Mrs. *(Pronounced "so-vay":)* Sové, our counselor, she smiles and asks if everything is OK.

CHORUS OF STUDENTS: I laughed at him when he was first out in dodgeball.
I cut in front of him at—I don't even remember when it was.
I wouldn't lend him a pencil when I had two extras.
(Dodgeball student:) Why didn't I just say "don't worry about it"?

HABIT: I want to say I don't think my friend is all right, but I just say "fine." "Fine, thanks."

CHORUS OF STUDENTS: I played keepaway with his backpack in seventh grade.
He'd smile at me in the lunch line sometimes.
(Keepaway student:) I didn't even know him.
(Smile at me student:) I wish I smiled back.

BRADY: I'm trying to be braver now—for as long as I can.

> *(Brady exits his bunker, squaring off with Dr. Copperfield.)*

MIRANDA: QE, this is your sister's night.

MELISSA: Yeah—we can totally shut this down.

MARNE: No.

MIRANDA: *(To Marne:)* You are totally outta this loop. QE, we can get this back.

QE: *(Beat. Shakes her head:)* I'll always love Beth, but there are other people in the world.

MIRANDA: *(To Marne:)* You think this is gonna make you more popular. It won't. *(To Melissa:)* Let's go.

(Miranda starts to exit. Melissa hesitates, then follows.)

DR. COPPERFIELD: *(Not unkindly:)* Come visit me on Monday, Brady.

BRADY: Jeremy was born on a Tuesday. He was a Capricorn. He didn't have any brothers and sisters.

LEGOLAS: When he was eight, he had the most awesome paper snake collection. Organized by species and families and colored in crayon.

SABRINA: He liked roses 'cause if you grabbed them wrong, you could prick your finger.

HABIT: He liked to skate, even though he couldn't stay on his board.

LEGOLAS: He tried to convince me that unicorns were real.

SABRINA: He tried to convince me he'd seen one.

HABIT: He tried to convince me he kept one in his backyard.

CHORUS OF STUDENTS: He was five-foot-eight and 130 pounds and he couldn't whistle —
He said he was the worst artist ever, but he wasn't even close.

SABRINA: He always smiled, even though I think sometimes it was just for everyone else.

CHORUS OF STUDENTS: He didn't have a lot of friends.
He deserved more.

And more smiles back.

He talked about silent movies.

And mountain ranges.

And dogs.

He said his favorite color was blue on Wednesdays but green on Fridays.

He never said what it was on the other days.

HEADLINE: And his favorite food was a cheeseburger, hold the cheese.

> *(This is the first normal sentence Headline has uttered in just over a year. It does not go unnoticed.)*

BRADY: And one Tuesday afternoon, he got too sad, more sad than he could take, and he went into his garage and left so many people behind, broken. We've spent a year trying to pick up all of our pieces, but there are so many of them it's hard to count and no matter how many I pick up, I always feel like there will be one missing.

LEGOLAS: Me too.

SABRINA: And me.

HABIT: And me.

MARNE: And me.

> *(Other members of the cast may chime in with "and me" as appropriate – particularly those who delivered lines about Jeremy – but it should end with Headline.)*

HEADLINE: And me.

ALISA: And a whole lot of people who just can't say the words. At least not yet.

> *(Brady gets up and walks over to Alisa. He takes her hand. Led by Brady and Alisa, all on stage exit with the exception of Luna,*

who has been there throughout the vigil and is revealed when the stage empties. She should now be much better lit.)

LUNA: Light travels at 186,000 miles per second. That's 671 million miles per hour. At that speed, you could travel completely around the earth's equator more than 7 times in a single second, or go back and forth between New York and Los Angeles 75 times. *(Beat.)* When light leaves the sun, it takes eight minutes to get to earth. That same light doesn't make it to Pluto, on average, until five and a half hours later. But it still comes. And I think sometimes it's easy to forget that on Pluto. It's easy to think that it'll be dark and cold forever. But the light's coming. Sometimes you just gotta hang on a little longer. 'Cause it always comes.

(Now that she's properly lit, it should be pretty obvious that Luna is Beth. Also, a simple sign that reads "And Jeremy" should now be a visible addition to the shrine, most likely added by Luna during the mass exit. The lights fade slowly until only the lights on the shrine remain, and then they too go out. End of play.)

The Author Speaks

What inspired you to write this play?
As of this writing, my most produced work is the anti-bullying play, *Thank You for Flushing My Head in the Toilet and other rarely used expressions*, and I occasionally do school visits associated with productions of it. In this particular case, I was working with the cast of a school in California's Mojave Desert that was touring it to local middle schools. Talking to their teacher, I learned that the discussions for my play and some of the issues it raises had triggered a whole lot of pent-up feelings among the cast about a series of events that had affected their school community in recent years. A popular student had died in some kind of off-roading accident, and it spawned all kinds of merchandising, things like bracelets and T-shirts to remember the deceased. At the same time, another student's suicide was completely ignored, to the point where the students felt that they had been deliberately denied the opportunity to talk about it. So when a school on Long Island (NY) commissioned me to write a new full-length play and left the topic open, it felt like the right time to write this one. While the world of *Locker* is most definitely entirely fictional, it's inspired by what happened at that school in the desert.

Was the structure of the play influenced by any other work?
Locker is episodic in nature, which I'm sure has something to do with the influence of film and TV, and most of my recent plays use that form, with many short scenes that push the action forward fairly rapidly and allow us to jump from place to place. Unlike a play such as *Dear Chuck*, though, which is a series of scenes and monologues that have a loose structure but largely cohere around a theme, *The Locker Next 2 Mine* tells its story in a relatively traditional way. Yes, there are some "out of time" moments, but by and large, the flow of the

plot is linear: a girl arrives in a new place, asks questions that those who live there had given up asking, and in doing so, forces members of the community to confront what's happened there. Or, in the words of Luna, "We're going to have to answer for our crimes against Pluto."

Have you dealt with the same theme in other works that you have written?
One of the major concerns in *The Locker Next 2 Mine* is teen suicide. It's the play of mine that deals with it most, but it's not the first. I've been nibbling around the edges of this important issue for some time. *Dear Chuck*'s "Three Rows" monologue talks about the seemingly inexplicable suicide of a student who had just set a soccer scoring record, while one of the two most prominent characters in *4 A.M.* is a teen who attempts suicide and then, with help from a stranger, pulls himself back from the brink. Unfortunately, it's one of those problems that just doesn't seem to go away, and so I continue to write about it—not that this play should be reduced to a play that is singularly about suicide, as there's a lot more going on than that.

What do you hope to achieve with this work?
My first goal, whenever I write a play, is to put a good story on stage and provide a worthy vehicle for talented performers and the production team. Having said that, I do hope that *The Locker Next 2 Mine* causes those in the communities where it gets produced to think a little about the idea of community. How can we each make our own little sphere a little more welcoming? In the play, reflecting upon her own guilt in Jeremy's suicide, a student says, "You think about every little thing—'cause maybe it was giant and you just couldn't see it." But that also means that sometimes the smallest gesture for good can be giant to someone who needs it.

What were the biggest challenges involved in the writing of this play?
This was a commissioned play, meaning that someone paid me ahead of time to write it in the hope of producing it. That production didn't actually happen. They had left the play topic wide open, which is usually a good thing, but it meant in this case that they hadn't warned me of any topics to avoid. So for all of the good things they had to say about the script, unfortunately it turned out that it hit a bit too close to home, as they'd experienced recent losses from both suicide and accidents, and with younger siblings and best friends still in the school population (and particularly in the class that would have staged it), they didn't want to reopen those still healing wounds. So they donated their opening weekend's royalties to Huntsville, Alabama's The Randolph School, which jumped in to stage the first production.

In terms of the actual writing of the play, there are always challenges when dealing with serious subjects. It's easy for the writing to become overwrought or precious, and I really wanted to avoid that. In particular, the ending got too long, and so both during the Alabama production and afterward when I was working on the one-act version at Soquel High School (Soquel, CA), I kept refining it to get it tighter, which meant mostly cutting—the Marne/Legolas/Brady triangle in particular was a challenge. But ultimately, less is almost always more. Another difficulty—and I love to write them— was writing the choral scenes, in which a whole series of characters will speak one after the other. Getting that rhythm right and finding the musicality of those moments always takes some experimenting.

Are any characters modeled after real life or historical figures?
Despite the fact that the play took its inspiration, as I mentioned earlier, from the bare bones facts of a real situation, the characters are entirely fictional. Having said that, Brady is named for a close friend, not because he's remotely like the Brady in the play—in fact he's completely the opposite—but simply because I have this habit of borrowing my friends' names for characters. So who knows—maybe if we become pals I'll name a character after you.

Shakespeare gave advice to the players in *Hamlet*; if you could give advice to your cast what would it be?
It's very easy to take plays on serious topics and turn them into doom and gloom fests: you are the production delivering the "important" message. Don't do it. Play against that. Yes, we know suicide and loss are serious topics, but they're already in the underlying structure of the play. Instead, it's important to find the comedy—there's plenty of it in the script—and let it out. It will make the serious moments play better, engage the audience more, and otherwise, you'll end up with something that is all one (somber) tone, leaving the audience wanting to (metaphorically, I hope) slit its own wrists. That would not be good. To me, plays are like pieces of music, which is important both when it comes to tone and also to rhythm. Much of this play wants to move, so let it move (which will again help you with tone)—except, for instance when it comes to the Pluto (and other) monologues, when it needs to stop for a moment. Don't be afraid of silence when you need it.

About the Author

Jonathan Dorf is a Los Angeles-based playwright, screenwriter, teacher and script consultant, whose plays have been produced in nearly every state in the US, as well as in Canada, Europe, Asia, Africa, Australia and New Zealand. He is Co-Chair of the Alliance of Los Angeles Playwrights and the Resident Playwriting Expert for Final Draft and The Writers Store. He directed the theatre program at The Haverford School and spent three years at Choate Rosemary Hall Summer Arts Conservatory as playwright-in-residence. A frequent guest artist at Thespian conferences and schools, he has served as Visiting Professor of Theatre in the MFA Playwriting and Children's Literature programs at Hollins University, and as United States cultural envoy to Barbados. He holds a BA in Dramatic Writing and Literature from Harvard College and an MFA in Playwriting from UCLA. He is a member of The Dramatists Guild and the Philadelphia Dramatists Center. Website: **http://jonathandorf.com.**

About YouthPLAYS

YouthPLAYS (www.youthplays.com) is a publisher of award-winning professional dramatists and talented new discoveries, each with an original theatrical voice, and all dedicated to expanding the vocabulary of theatre for young actors and audiences. On our website you'll find one-act and full-length plays and musicals for teen and pre-teen (and even college) actors, as well as duets and monologues for competition. Many of our authors' works have been widely produced at high schools and middle schools, youth theatres and other TYA companies, both amateur and professional, as well as at elementary schools, camps, churches and other institutions serving young audiences and/or actors worldwide. Most are intended for performance by young people, while some are intended for adult actors performing for young audiences.

YouthPLAYS was co-founded by professional playwrights Jonathan Dorf and Ed Shockley. It began merely as an additional outlet to market their own works, which included a substantial body of award-winning published and unpublished plays and musicals. Those interested in their published plays were directed to the respective publishers' websites, and unpublished plays were made available in electronic form. But when they saw the desperate need for material for young actors and audiences—coupled with their experience that numerous quality plays for young people weren't finding a home—they made the decision to represent the work of other playwrights as well. Dozens and dozens of authors are now members of the YouthPLAYS family, with scripts available both electronically and in traditional acting editions. We continue to grow as we look for exciting and challenging plays and musicals for young actors and audiences.

About ProduceaPlay.com

Let's put up a play! Great idea! But producing a play takes time, energy and knowledge. While finding the necessary time and energy is up to you, ProduceaPlay.com is a website designed to assist you with that third element: knowledge.

Created by YouthPLAYS' co-founders, Jonathan Dorf and Ed Shockley, ProduceaPlay.com serves as a resource for producers at all levels as it addresses the many facets of production. As Dorf and Shockley speak from their years of experience (as playwrights, producers, directors and more), they are joined by a group of award-winning theatre professionals and experienced teachers from the world of academic theatre, all making their expertise available for free in the hope of helping this and future generations of producers, whether it's at the school or university level, or in community or professional theatres.

The site is organized into a series of major topics, each of which has its own page that delves into the subject in detail, offering suggestions and links for further information. For example, Publicity covers everything from Publicizing Auditions to How to Use Social Media to Posters to whether it's worth hiring a publicist. Casting details Where to Find the Actors, How to Evaluate a Resume, Callbacks and even Dealing with Problem Actors. You'll find guidance on your Production Timeline, The Theater Space, Picking a Play, Budget, Contracts, Rehearsing the Play, The Program, House Management, Backstage, and many other important subjects.

The site is constantly under construction, so visit often for the latest insights on play producing, and let it help make your play production dreams a reality.

More from YouthPLAYS

Dear Chuck by Jonathan Dorf
Dramedy. 30-40 minutes. 8-30+ performers (gender flexible).

Teenagers are caught in the middle—they're not quite adults, but they're definitely no longer children. Through a series of scenes and monologues, we meet an eclectic group of teen characters who are trying to communicate with that wannabe special someone, coping with a classmate's suicide, battling controlling parents, swimming for that island of calm in the stormy sea of technology—and many others. What they all have in common is the search for their "Chuck," that elusive moment of knowing who you are. Also available in a 60-70 minute version.

Boys vs. Girls: Armageddon by Adam J. Goldberg
Dramedy. 38-55 minutes. 5 males, 6-8 females, plus non-speaking roles (11-60+ performers.)

It's war! Nobody's quite sure how it started, but all the town's girls and boys have split up along strict gender lines and are determined to crush the opposition utterly. As water balloons fly and rumors of cootie-laced biological weapons circulate, it's up to best friends Terry and Samantha to break the gender barrier and avert mutual assured destruction.

Outside the Box by Bradley Hayward
Dramedy. 25-35 minutes. 12 either.

Thinking outside the box isn't always easy, especially when the world requires you to live on the inside. Exhausted from cramming into corners where they do not fit, six teenagers turn things inside out by inviting others to see things from a whole new perspective—outside to a world where balloons change color, brooms become dance partners, and kites fly without a string.

Long Joan Silver by Arthur M. Jolly
Comedy. 90-100 minutes. 6-15 males, 8-20 females (14-30 performers possible, plus extras).

The classic adventure tale of buried treasure—and the original one-legged pirate with a parrot—gets a timely makeover, combining offbeat farce, sight gags and horrendous puns with a dramatic core that explores discrimination, privilege and greed. Unlike in Robert Louis Stevenson's book, where only one unnamed character is female, women are front and center as *Long Joan Silver*'s young Jim Hawkins comes of age during the fateful voyage of the Hispaniola and the clash between an all-female pirate crew and Squire Trelawney, Doctor Livesey and the domineering Captain Smollett.

Aesop Refabled by Nicole B. Adkins, Jeff Goode, Adam Hahn, Samantha Macher, Liz Shannon Miller, Dominic Mishler, Mike Rothschild and Dave Ulrich
Comedy. 45-60 minutes. 3-11 males, 3-11 females (3-21 performers possible).

One of L.A.'s edgiest theatre companies brings a modern spin to Aesop's classic yarns, as eight timeless fables get a 21st century reboot. Cupcake bullies, tween warriors, scheming cheerleaders and apocalyptic yellow butterfly people... Each tale takes an unexpected twist in this innovative offering!

screens by Jessica McGettrick
Dramedy. 35-45 minutes. 3 males, 7 females, 30 either (10-40 performers possible).

In *screens*, we see the world through the eyes of a gamer, a lonely person looking for love, a music fan, a blogger, a bully's target and many others as they discover the perils and pleasures of creating an online persona that is different from their offline reality. What would you say if no one could see you behind the computer screen? Who would you become?

The Mystic Tale of Aladdin by Randy Wyatt
Fantasy. 50-60 minutes. 9 females.

Seven princesses wait to hear which of them the Sultan has chosen for his bride. To pass the final minutes before he announces his decision, the maidens tell the tale of Aladdin, a tale each claims as her country's own. Filled with magic, adventure, intrigue and romance, this all-female version of the classic story packs a powerful message of empowering young women to fulfill their own wishes.

Nobody's Listening by Ed Shockley
Dramedy. 50-60 minutes. 3 males, 3 females, plus extras.

A film crew sets up to broadcast a live performance of a new television pilot, *The Adventures of Mech-Boy.* As the audience files in, there is panic onstage because the actor playing the Robot star of the anti-violence show has gotten caught in his trailer. The frantic director recruits a kid from the audience to replace the star seconds before the broadcast begins, but the impromptu actor becomes increasingly uncooperative and comically inventive as he struggles to make the hokey show reflect the real challenges that youth face in the difficult environment of a public school.

Teen Mogul by Lucy Wang
Dramedy. 75-90 minutes. 5-16 males, 3-13 females (8-20 performers possible).

Tracy's life is turned upside down when her mother walks out. Her father can't cope, her brother's too young, and they're about to lose their home. But if Steve Jobs once called the president of Hewlett-Packard while he was still in high school, why can't Tracy call her favorite mogul and ask for a job? With a little push from her English teacher, Tracy leaps for the brass ring, but it's going to take some unlikely allies to help her navigate the prickly paths of success and save her family, her house and herself in this play inspired by a true story.